SCHEMATIC WI
SIMPLIFIED

STEP-BY-STE

Stanley H. Aglow

Business News Publishing Company
Troy, Michigan

Library of Congress Cataloging in Publication Data
Aglow, Stanley H., 1927—
    Schematic Wiring Simplified, step-by-step

    1. Electric apparatus and appliances—
    Maintenance and repair.   2. Electric wiring—
    Diagrams.
I. Title
TK452.A34   683'.83   83-2736
ISBN 0-912524-23-5

Printed in the United States of America

CONTENTS

Section I

INTRODUCTION

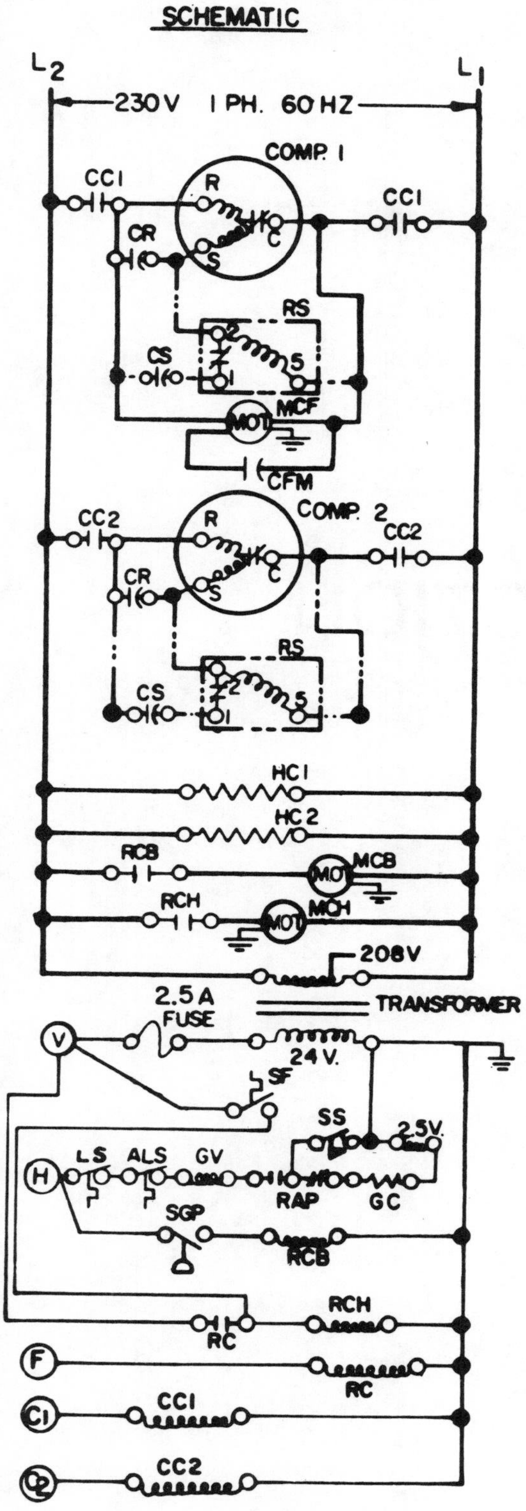

SCHEMATIC

ELECTRICAL SCHEMATICS

The schematic, Figure 1-1, is the engineer's blueprint of an electrical circuit. It differs from a builder's blueprint in that it does not show the actual location of the electrical devices used in the circuit, but only the electrical relationship of one device to the other.

Figure 1-2a is a somewhat realistic drawing of a light bulb, with a cord, plug and switch. Figure 1-2b is an electrical schematic of the same light bulb, cord, plug and switch. Instead of a plug, this drawing uses L_1 and N as the power source, and uses a single pole, single throw (SPST) switch to control the current flow in one conductor to turn the light on and off. From the schematic, you can see how the switch is wired into the circuit while the pictorial representation shows only the location of each device in the circuit. You can see that this additional information makes the schematic invaluable when troubleshooting a circuit.

The schematic, which is sometimes called a ladder drawing, uses symbols and abbreviations in an unusual type of shorthand. The meaning of these symbols and abbreviations is usually spelled out in a feature of the schematic called the Legend.

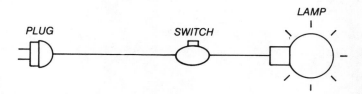

FIG. 1-2a. Pictorial drawing of a lamp circuit.

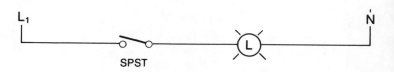

FIG. 1-1. Typical schematic diagram. *Courtesy Fedders Corp.*

FIG. 1-2b. Schematic equivalent of the pictorial drawing, Figure 1-2a.

The Legend

The legend or key should list all the devices and abbreviations appearing in the schematic, Figure 1-3, and give a concise description or function of any special controls. The legend may also include timing settings and other necessary information.

You will find that there are a variety of abbreviations for the same device. Carrier abbreviates indoor fan relay IFR while York uses R and Westinghouse uses FR.

You may also find a variety of designations for the same device. Carrier will use an interchangeable holding relay (HR) and a reversing relay (RVR). While they have differing functions, both relays have 208/240v coils and two sets of normally open and normally closed contacts. Thus, they are alike in everything except name and function, and can be used interchangeably.

There may be notes giving additional information such as as exceptions, changes in wiring for varying voltages, motor protection devices being used, wires that must be altered when changing motor speeds, plus additional information that is valuable when troubleshooting or installing the equipment.

An important part of the legend, especially for the installer, is the wiring identification which is basically the same for all manufacturers:

——————— Heavy black line
(High voltage, factory wired)
——————— Light black line
(Low voltage, factory wired)
-------- Heavy broken line
(High voltage, field wired)
------------- Light broken line
(Low voltage, field wired)

```
CC   - CONTACTOR COMPRESSOR
COMP - COMPRESSOR
CFM  - CAPACITOR FAN MOTOR
CR   - CAPACITOR RUN (COMP.)
CS   - CAPACITOR START (COMP.)
GV   - GAS VALVE
HC   - HEATER COMPRESSOR
LS   - LIMIT SWITCH
MCB  - MOTOR COMBUSTION BLOWER
MCF  - MOTOR CONDENSER FAN
MCH  - MOTOR HEATING/COOLING BLOWER
RAP  - RELAY AUTO PILOT
RCB  - RELAY COMBUSTION BLOWER
RCH  - RELAY COOLING/HEATING BLOWER
RS   - RELAY START
SF   - SWITCH FAN
SGP  - SWITCH PILOT GAS PRESSURE
SS   - SWITCH SAIL
GC   - GLOW COIL
ASL  - AUXILIARY LIMIT SWITCH
RC   - RELAY COOLING
```

FIG. 1-3. Legend accompanying the Figure 1-1 schematic. *Courtesy Fedders Corp.*

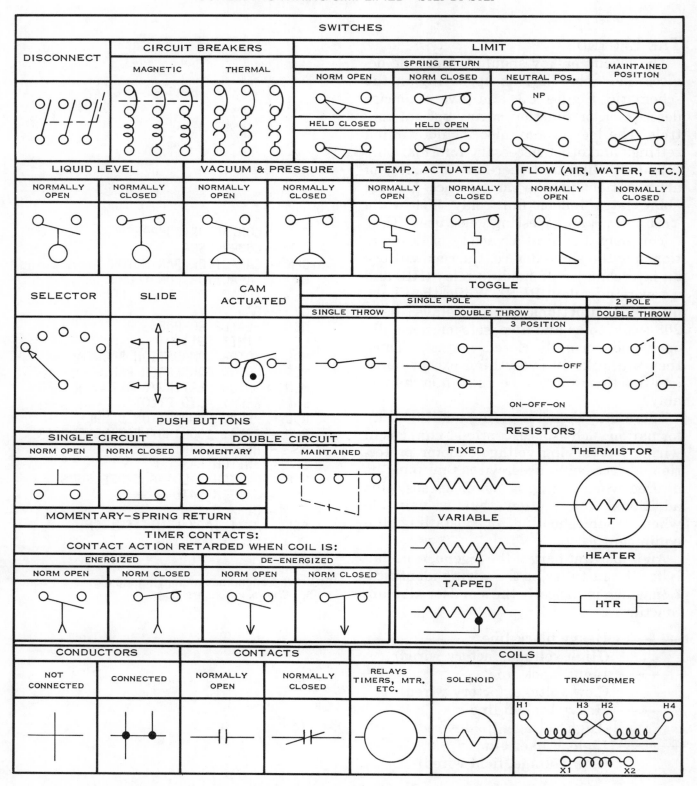

FIG. 1-4. Typical graphic symbols for electrical schematics. *Courtesy York Division, Borg-Warner Corp.*

SYMBOLS

The schematic makes use of many standard electrical graphic symbols. Each manufacturer may prefer slight variations, but they are all basically the same.

The combination of the graphic symbols and the abbreviations found in the legend form an electrical shorthand system which, when mastered, will allow you to troubleshoot electrical circuits much faster and with fewer errors. Some of these symbols are shown in Figures 1-4 and 1-5. Notice that there is a descriptive relationshipship between the symbol and the device.

Contacts, in a control, are shown in their normal position. The normal position assumes that the system is off or de-energized. Thus, the normal position of an electromagnetic relay, when its coil is de-energized, is with the contacts open.

The normal position for a pressure control assumes that it is affected by atmospheric pressure only. When the pressure control is installed, it will open or close as the pressure in the system changes.

Flow switches, whether gas or liquid, are in their normal position when no liquid is moving. Movement of the liquid will cause the contacts to change position.

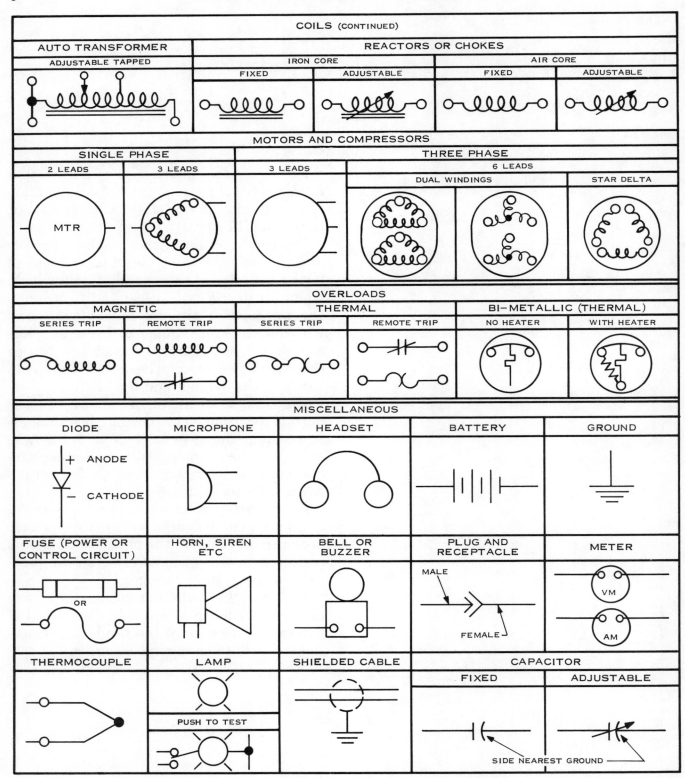

FIG. 1-5. Typical graphic symbols for electrical schematics. *Courtesy York Division, Borg-Warner Corp.*

The position of the moveable element of the contact symbol has a specific meaning, Figure 1-6:

1. A moveable contact that is open and below the fixed contact indicates that the switch closes on an increase in temperature, pressure, etc.
2. A moveable contact that is closed and below the fixed contact indicates that the switch opens on a decrease in temperature, pressure, etc.
3. A moveable contact that is open and above the fixed contact indicates that the switch closes on a decrease in temperature, pressure, etc.
4. A moveable contact that is closed and above the fixed contact indicates that the switch opens on an increase in temperature, pressure, etc.

You should spend as much time as necessary to commit these symbols to memory. Some manufacturers of heating, cooling and refrigeration equipment do not show the symbols in their service manuals and most mechanics do not have a copy of the symbols in their tool box. Without understanding the symbols, troubleshooting becomes impossible.

SYMBOL	NAME	CONTACT POSITION	FORCE
	LOW PRESSURE SWITCH	NO	CLOSES ON INCREASE IN REFRIGERANT PRESSURE
	HIGH PRESSURE SWITCH	NC	OPENS ON INCREASE IN REFRIGERANT PRESSURE
	COOLING THERMOSTAT	NO	CLOSES ON RISE IN TEMPERATURE
	HEATING THERMOSTAT	NC	OPENS ON RISE IN TEMPERATURE
	LIQUID LEVEL SWITCH	NO	CLOSES ON RISE IN LIQUID LEVEL
	LIQUID LEVEL SWITCH	NC	OPENS ON RISE IN LIQUID LEVEL
	FLOW SWITCH LIQUID OR AIR	NO	CLOSES ON FLOW OR MOVEMENT
	FLOW SWITCH LIQUID OR AIR	NC	OPENS ON FLOW OR MOVEMENT

FIG. 1-6. Interpreting symbols for moveable contacts.

Section II

BASIC ELECTRICITY
AND DEVICES

This section is not intended to be an in-depth study of each electrical device. Rather it serves to explain and show how each device will function in an electrical circuit.

MAGNETISM AND MAGNETS

Magnetism, the operating force behind all electromagnetic relays, motors and solenoids, can be either permanently available or electrically produced.

Permanent magnets are created by exposing a bar of hardened steel to a strong magnetic field. The force of this field permanently aligns the molecules in the bar, giving them magnetic polarity. When the strong magnetic force is removed, the bar will continue to retain its magnetism.

Permanent magnets are commonly used as cabinet and refrigerator latches. Other permanent magnets are used in thermostats and switches to assure snap action. The permanent magnet rarely becomes a source of trouble.

An electromagnet is created by wrapping a coil of wire around a soft iron core, Figure 2-1. When current is passed through the coil of wire, the soft iron core becomes strongly magnetized. On the other hand, if the current ceases, the iron core instantly loses its magnetism. The ability to quickly magnetize and demagnetize the iron core permits remote operation of many of the controls used in heating, cooling and refrigeration.

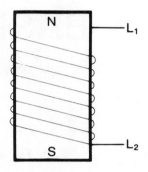

FIG. 2-1. An electromagnet is created by wrapping a coil of wire around a soft iron core.

SOLENOIDS

Most electromagnets, such as those used in relays, have a fixed coil and a fixed core. The solenoid, on the other hand, is an electromagnet with a fixed coil and a moveable core, Figure 2-2.

In one typical application, Figure 2-3, the solenoid is used to open and close a gas valve. When current is supplied to the coil, the iron core is electromagnetically drawn into the center of the coil, thereupon opening the valve. When the current is interrupted, the magnetic field is lost and the core drops, often of its own weight, to again close the valve.

Solenoid valves operate on voltages ranging from less than one volt to over 440v, in a widespread band of applications, Figure 2-4.

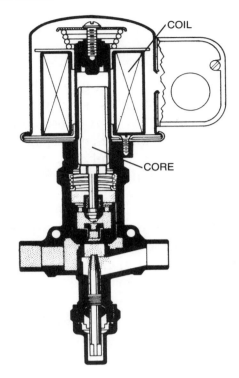

FIG. 2-3. A solenoid operated gas valve. *Courtesy ITT General Controls.*

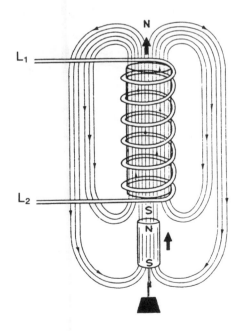

FIG. 2-2. A solenoid is an electromagnet with a moveable soft iron core.

FIG. 2-4. A solenoid used for refrigerant flow control. *Courtesy Alco Controls Div., Emerson Electric Co.*

TRANSFORMERS

In refrigeration, cooling, and heating applications, it is often necessary to use voltages lower or higher than those supplied by the electric utilities. It is necessary, then, to modify this power supply to create the required voltage. The least expensive way to do this is with a transformer, Figure 2-5.

The transformer is constructed with two unconnected windings, a primary and a secondary, usually wound on a core of magnetic material. An alternating current, when applied to the primary, will induce voltage in the secondary winding.

Having less turns in the secondary than in the primary will produce a step-down transformer, used for low voltage thermostats and control circuits. A transformer having more turns in the secondary than in the primary will produce a step-up transformer, such as 10,000 volts used for oil burner ignition.

Due to coil resistance losses in the transformer, the voltage times amps (va) of the primary and secondary coils are not equal, making the transformer less than 100% efficient. These losses must be considered when sizing a transformer. The secondary will need to have enough electrical energy to drive the connected load. System equipment and amperage ratings must be considered in selecting the proper transformer.

Consider the secondary of the transformer the same as the service entrance cable to your home. The size of this cable is based on the amperage draw (60a, 100a, 150a, 200a, etc.) at the voltage (120v, 208v, 240v, etc.) to operate all of the electrical equipment in your home.

FIG. 2-5. Step-down transformer with mounting plate. *Courtesy Honeywell Inc.*

The transformer volts × amps (va) is also figured this way. Adding the amperage rating on each magnetic relay coil, solenoid, etc., will give you the total current draw of the entire system. Multiplying this total by the voltage necessary, such as 24v, will give you the total va required.

Transformers must meet two requirements:

1. The transformer must be capable of pulling in all magnetic devices, at once, under inrush or starting conditions.
2. The transformer must be capable of carrying the continuous current draw of all components, without overheating.

Considering that the transformer is the same as the power supply, the wire used in the secondary or low voltage circuit must be properly sized to prevent a voltage drop at the loads.

Because transformers have no physical connection between the primary and secondary coils, the coils can be checked, with an ohmmeter, for open or shorted windings. A transformer's output voltage that is within 10% of its rating is considered to be good.

Transformers that operate on more than one primary voltage, such as 120v or 208v or 240v, are called tapped transformers. Various primary voltages may be applied by tapping the transformer primary at selected points within its length, Figure 2-6. Each tap will produce 24v because the secondary output is determined by the ratio of the number of turns in the primary and secondary coils.

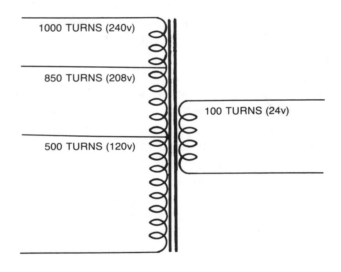

FIG. 2-6. A tapped transformer that produces 24v from a variety of primary voltages.

$$\frac{\text{secondary turns}}{\text{primary turns}} \times \text{primary voltage} = \text{secondary volts}$$

$$\frac{100}{1000} \times 240v = 24v$$

$$\frac{100}{850} \times 208v = 24v$$

$$\frac{100}{500} \times 120v = 24v$$

RELAYS

The electromagnetic relay, Figure 2-7, is a magnetically operated switch. A typical relay will consist of a low (24v) voltage electromagnet and one or more sets of high (115v/230v) voltage contacts.

The contacts may be normally open or normally closed, or a combination of NO and NC contacts. When the electromagnet is energized, all the contacts in the relay are reversed: that is, all NC contacts open and all NO contacts close. When the relay is de-energized, all contacts return to their normal position, whether open or closed.

The photo shows that the relay coil and contacts are both mounted on a common base and a wiring diagram will show both the coil and contacts in the same location. However, a schematic diagram will often separate the coil from the contacts to show the coil in the low voltage circuit and the contacts in the high voltage circuit.

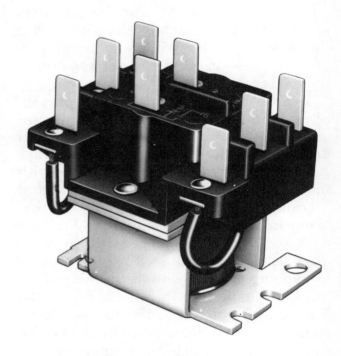

FIG. 2-7. Electromagnetic relay with two sets of NO and two sets of NC contacts. *Courtesy Essex Controls.*

CONTACTOR AND MOTOR STARTER

The contactor, Figure 2-8, which is basically a relay, is used to make and break the power supply to the compressor. If the contact points are rated high enough, the condenser fan motor may also be wired through the contactor, parallel to the compressor, to start both the condenser fan and the compressor at the same time. Contactors are used for switching heavy current loads or high voltage or both. Because the coil is isolated from the contacts, a low, 24v or 120v voltage can be supplied to the coil, and 208v, 240v, 277v, 480v can be supplied through the contacts to the load.

A motor starter is basically a contactor with the addition of overload heaters.

FIG. 2-8. A contactor for switching on motors or resistive loads. *Courtesy Honeywell Inc.*

POTENTIAL MAGNETIC STARTING RELAY

The potential or voltage starting relay, Figure 2-9, is used on single phase, capacitor start, hermetic compressors, to close a circuit to the phase or starting winding, until the motor reaches approximately 80% of its rated speed and then opens the circuit to the phase winding.

The potential relay consists of a fine wire electromagnetic coil, with a voltage rating above line voltage. The contact points are normally closed, completing a circuit, through the start capacitor, from the run to start terminals on the compressor.

When the motor starts, counter-EMF or back voltage quickly increases in the starting winding. This causes an increase in voltage through the relay coil which is wired between the common and start terminals on the compressor. When the rated voltage of the relay coil is reached, the coil becomes an electromagnet, opening the normally closed contacts.

During the running cycle, the back voltage remains high enough to hold the contacts open. If the motor slows down because of a heavy load, a defective run capacitor, or the motor circuit is opened, the voltage feeding the potential relay coil will drop rapidly, de-energizing the coil and permitting the relay contacts to close.

FIG. 2-9. A potential magnetic starting relay. *Courtesy Essex Controls.*

CURRENT MAGNETIC STARTING RELAY

The current or amperage starting relay, Figure 2-10, is used on fractional horsepower, single phase, hermetic compressors. The relay closes a circuit to the phase or starting winding until the motor reaches approximately ⅔ or ¾ of its rated speed, then opens the circuit to the starting winding.

Current relays consist of a heavy wire coil and a set of normally open contacts.

When a circuit to the motor is closed, all current is fed to the main or running winding, passing through the start relay coil. Since the running winding, alone, cannot start the motor, a locked rotor condition exists, causing high amperage or current to flow through the motor winding and the relay coil. This high current produces a strong magnetic field in the relay coil, closing the normally open contacts. With the contacts closed, a circuit is now complete to the starting winding, starting the motor. As the motor approaches its rated speed, the current draw of the motor drops and the coil's magnetic field becomes too weak to hold the contacts closed, the contacts now open, breaking the circuit to the start winding. The relay contacts stay closed for only a few seconds each time the motor starts.

FIG. 2-10. Current magnetic starting relay. *Courtesy Texas Instruments, Inc.*

INDOOR FAN RELAY

A relay that seems to be difficult to understand is the indoor fan relay. This relay consists of an electromagnetic coil and a set of normally open and normally closed contacts.

The fan relay is used to start the indoor or evaporator fan whenever the cooling compressor starts. If the evaporator blower does not start, the evaporator could freeze up and possibly ruin the compressor. When an air conditioning system is added to an existing furnace, a fan relay must be installed.

The normally open contacts of the fan relay, Figure 2-11, must be wired parallel to the the plenum switch. The normally closed contacts must be wired in series with the plenum switch.

When the thermostat calls for heat, the fan is cycled by the temperature actuated plenum switch which closes at approximately 140°F. Power is supplied to the fan through the normally closed contacts in the indoor fan relay after the plenum switch is closed.

When cooling is called for, 24v power is supplied to the indoor fan relay coil. Energizing the coil causes the normally closed contacts to open and the normally open contacts to close, thereby bypassing the plenum switch and activating the fan which is now controlled by the cooling thermostat.

A fan relay can be used to select the desired speed from a two-speed motor. as shown in Figure 2-12, the fan relay selects low speed while heating and high speed while cooling and prevents both speeds from being energized simultaneously which could destroy the motor.

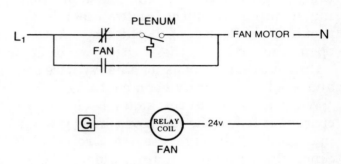

FIG. 2-11. Schematic of an indoor fan relay.

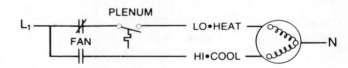

FIG. 2-12. Indoor fan relay can select the desired speed from a two-speed motor.

FAN CENTER

The fan center is a relay with a built-in 24v step-down transformer, Figure 2-13. Thus, it has more wires to confuse you.

When installing a fan center, connect the primary of the transformer to the 120v or higher line power supply, L_1 and N. Connect the secondary or 24v side of the transformer to thermostat terminal R or common. Connect the fan center relay coil to thermostat terminal G which is the fan terminal. Connect the normally closed contacts in series with the the furnace plenum switch and the normally open contacts to the fan motor. Both sets of contacts are in the line voltage circuit.

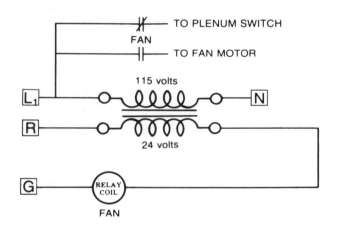

FIG. 2-13. Schematic of a fan center.

Impedance or Lock Out Relay

Impedence relays, Figure 2-14, are used in refrigeration and air conditioning systems to provide a lockout circuit and remote manual reset. When a safety control such as a high or low pressure switch, motor overload, oil safety switch, etc., opens, the lockout circuit will prevent the system from starting, even after all safety control contacts close. By locking out the control circuit, the system can be checked to determine the cause before more damage is done.

The relay consists of a set of normally closed contacts wired in series with the safety controls and the compressor contactor coil, Figure 2-15. The impedence coil is wired in series with the contactor coil and parallel to the relay's normally closed contacts and the closed contacts of the safety controls.

During normal operation, the normally closed contacts of the relay and the safety controls present a course of least resistance, permitting full voltage to energize the contactor coil.

If one of the pressure controls or overloads opens, the shunt circuit to the contactor is broken, energizing the impedance coil. The resistance of the impedance coil is so high that there is not enough voltage to the contactor coil to hold in the contactor contacts. As the impedance relay pulls in, its normally closed contacts open, locking out the circuit to the contactor coil even though the safety controls may have reset.

The system will remain locked out and can only be started again by breaking the circuit to the contactor coil. This is usually done by moving the thermostat control switch to the off or reset position and then back to cool.

FIG. 2-14. Impedence or lock out relay. *Courtesy Honeywell Inc.*

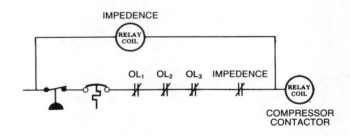

FIG. 2-15. In an impedence relay circuit, the impedence coil is wired in series with compressor contactor coil and parallel to the relay's normally closed contacts.

THERMAL TIME DELAY RELAY

The thermal time delay relay, Figure 2-16, consists of a heater coil wound on a bimetal element and a set of normally open or normally closed contacts, Figure 2-17. The heater element may be had in many different voltages, such as 24v, 120v, 208v, 240v, etc. Because there is no internal electrical connection between the heater and the contacts, the voltage used for the heater circuit (24v) may be different from the voltage going through the contacts, (240v).

After a time delay, the heater is warmed, causing the bimetal element to bend, closing or opening the contacts, depending on the application, with a snap action. Snap action is accomplished by using a small permanent magnet. This action prevents chattering or arcing of the contact points on make and break.

Time delay relays are used to prevent two or more compressors in one system from starting at the same moment, thereby eliminating the excessive inrush of current, or to assure that the water pump starts before the compressor in a water-cooled system, Figure 2-18.

Time delay relays are used on electric resistance furnaces or heaters to bring on each heat strip in sequence, preventing excessive inrush of current which would happen if all the strips are energized at once.

Time delay relays of approximately four to five minute delay are used to prevent short cycling of a hermetic compressor after it has been shut down due to the action of the safety controls or thermostat. The relay will not permit the compressor to start for four to five minutes, reducing the chances of overheating the hermetic compressor motor and preventing a possible burnout. Time delay relays are also used to control incremental starting of large three-phase motors.

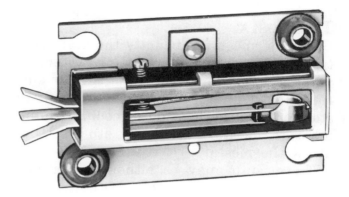

FIG. 2-16. Cutaway of a thermal time delay heater. *Courtesy Essex Controls.*

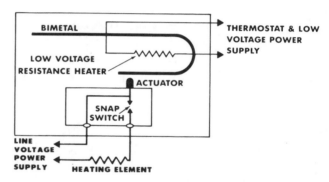

FIG. 2-17. Schematic of a thermal time delay heater. *Courtesy Honeywell Inc.*

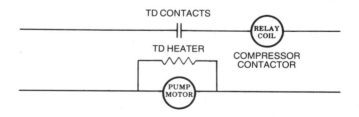

FIG. 2-18. When the water pump contacts (not shown) close, both the water pump and thermal time delay (TD) heater are energized. 60 seconds later, the heater will warp closed the TD contacts and complete a circuit to the compressor contactor relay. In this example, line voltage is supplied to both the TD heater and the TD contacts.

Thermostats

The thermostat is usually the main controller of the heating or cooling system. It will sense the temperature of the air surrounding it and open or close a circuit to start or stop the heating or cooling equipment, to maintain the temperature setting at the thermostat.

Thermostats may be either line or low voltage; however, low voltage thermostats are most often used in residential applications. The low voltage thermostat has better control characteristics, is easier and less expensive to install, and is safer to use in the home.

The most widely used heat responsive material, that will react to make and break the control circuit, is the bimetal element, Figure 2-19. The bimetal consists of two thin strips of dissimilar metals that are bonded together to form a thin sandwich. When heated, one metal has a higher rate of expansion than the other. Exposed to heat, the two metals will expand at different rates. This expanding or stretching at different rates, at the same temperature, will cause the bimetal to bend or warp. If one end of the strip is anchored, the other end will bend enough to open or close a set of contacts, as the temperature around the bimetal changes.

The bimetal may have the contacts connected to it and carry the electrical load or a small permanant magnet may be used to assure snap action by a separate set of contacts.

One popular method is to enclose a drop of mercury in a glass bulb that is attached to a coiled bimetal element, Figure 2-19. Changing the position of the bulb will cause the the mercury to move and open or close a set of contacts that are bridged by the mercury.

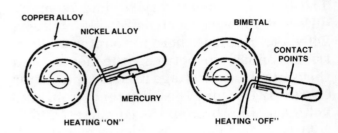

FIG. 2-19. When the bimetal contracts, on a fall in temperature, the mercurcy in the bulb bridges the two contacts to complete the heating circuit. *Courtesy Honeywell Inc.*

FIG. 2-20. Heating/cooling thermostats employ a subbase that permits the selection of heating or cooling and automatic or constant fan operation. *Courtesy Honeywell Inc.*

Unlike the straight bimetal, that can be mounted in any position, the mercury bulb must be mounted upright and level for proper performance.

The heating/cooling thermostat usually comes with a subbase, Figure 2-20, equipped with Heat, Off, Cool positions and provision for constant or automatic indoor fan operation. With the thermostat on Cool, the indoor or evaporator fan must also be on, to prevent the evaporator from frosting. With the thermostat on Heat, the indoor fan must start when the furnace plenum temperature reaches 140°. In the Auto position, the indoor fan operates in tandem with the heating and cooling systems. In the On position, the fan will run constantly, even with the other systems in the standby mode.

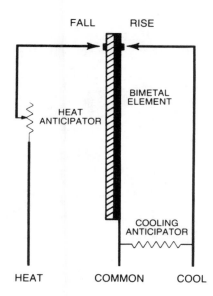

FIG. 2-21. Schematic of a bimetal switch with heating and cooling anticipation.

To provide a more comfortable room temperature, thermostats will usually have heating and cooling anticipation, Figure 2-21. Heating anticipation is accomplished by wiring a small variable heating resistor in series with the heating contacts in the thermostat. The anticipator, set to match the amperage rating of the primary control, will add heat to the bimetal element when the heating contacts close. This added heat, plus the room temperature, will cause the heating contacts to open before the room comes up to the thermostat setting. The residual heat in the heater will bring the room up to the thermostat setting, preventing the overheating of the room.

The cooling anticipator is a fixed resistor, wired parallel to the cooling contacts. This anticipator adds heat to the bimetal element when the cooling contacts are open. The added heat, plus the rising room temperature, will cause the cooling contacts to close a little before the actual room temperature comes up to the cut-in setting. When the cooling contacts close, the cooling anticipator is bypassed and the cooling contacts will open when the air temperature drops to the thermostat cut-out set point.

Because the heating anticipator is wired in series with the heating contacts, a break in the anticipator element will cause a shutdown of the heating system. A break in the cooling anticipator, wired parallel to the cooling contacts, will not cause a shutdown of the cooling system.

PRESSURE CONTROLS

High and low pressure controls, Figures 2-22 and 2-23, are used as safety limits in cooling and refrigeration systems. Low pressure controls are also used as motor cycling controls in refrigeration equipment.

As a limit protector, the high side pressure control opens the compressor power circuit on an above normal pressure, to prevent excessive pressure in the condenser. The low side pressure control opens the power circuit to the compressor on a decrease in normal pressure, to prevent the evaporator temperature, in an air conditioner, from falling below the point at which frost would form on the coil. The low pressure control will also cut out the compressor upon loss of the refrigerant.

Pressure controls come with automatic or manual reset. Automatic reset will restart the system when the pressure returns to the cut-in setting on the control. The pressure switch used depends upon the construction of the equipment and the preference of the manufacturer.

All safety controls should be set to the manufacturer's specification.

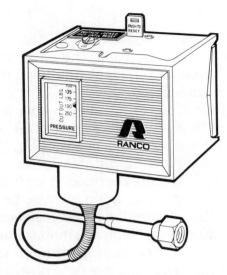

FIG. 2-22. High pressure control. *Courtesy Ranco Controls.*

FIG. 2-23. Low pressure control. *Courtesy Ranco Controls.*

FIG. 2-24. Resistors in series.

RESISTORS IN SERIES

Figure 2-24 shows four resistors in a series circuit: a 388 ohm center vertical drier, a pair of defrost heaters totaling 25 ohms and a 47,000 ohm defrost thermostat resistor. This circuit is typical of one found in a frost-free refrigerator.

The theory of how these resistors are utilized is somewhat complex and outside the scope of this book. Therefore, we will give you some simple rules of thumb, then explain how the resistors operate in this circuit.

The first rule is this: *High resistance produces little heat, low resistance produces maximum heat.* Therefore, if we want maximum heat production by the two 12½ ohm defrost heaters, we have to take the 47,000 ohm defrost thermostat resistor and the 388 ohm center vertical drier out of the circuit.

The second rule is this: *The heat produced by each of a series of resistors is directly proportional to the resistance of each heater.* Therefore, the 47,000 ohm heater will produce 99% of the heat in the four-resistor circuit. This amount of heat is, for our purposes, insignificant, being only 0.3 watts.

Actually, the 47,000 ohm resistor has no functional purpose in this circuit. It is only there to permit continuity testing through the defrost thermostat.

Since the current in a simple electric circuit is dependent on the applied voltage and the total resistance of the circuit, the total resistance of this circuit is

or
$$R_T = R_1 + R_2 + R_3 + R_4$$
$$R_T = 388 + 12.5 + 12.5 + 47,000 = 47,413$$

Therefore, in solving this simple circuit, use the formula

$$\frac{E}{R} = I$$

$$\frac{115v}{47,413 \text{ ohms}} = .0024 \text{ amps}$$

To find the watts produced, use the formula

$$\text{volts} \times \text{amps} = \text{watts}$$
$$115 \text{ volts} \times .0024 \text{ amps} = .276 \text{ watts}$$

When the defrost thermostat closes, bypassing the 47,000 ohm resistor, the contacts on the defrost timer change position and bypass the 388 ohm center vertical drier. Now find the wattage for the defrost heaters.

$$\frac{E}{R} = I$$

$$\frac{115v}{25 \text{ ohms}} = 4.6 \text{ amps}$$

$$\text{volts} \times \text{amps} = \text{watts}$$
$$115v \times 4.6 \text{ amps} = 529 \text{ watts}$$

CAPACITORS

Capacitors are used to improve the starting and running torque of split phase motors and hermetic compressors used for air conditioning and refrigeration.

The three types of motors that use capacitors are: the capacitor start, the capacitor run, and the permanent split capacitor (PSC).

There are several types of capacitors in use, but the electrolytic, Figure 2-25, and the oil-filled, Figure 2-26, are the most popular with the heating and cooling industry.

The electrolytic or start capacitor is used to improve the starting torque of the motor. Due to the high current that must pass through the capacitor while starting, the start capacitor is not recommended for continuous duty and must be removed from the circuit by a centrifugal switch, current relay, potential relay, or thermal relay when the motor attains approximately ¾ of its rated speed.

The oil-filled or run capacitor is used with permanent split capacitor motors to improve the running torque. Its design and lower microfarad rating allow the run capacitor to remain in the circuit without overloading or capacitor failure.

The unit of capacitance is the farad. Capacitors are usually rated in microfarads (mfd) or one-millionth of a farad.

FIG. 2-25. Electrolytic or start capacitor. *Courtesy Sprague Electric Co.*

FIG. 2-26. Oil-filled or run capacitor. *Courtesy Sprague Electric Co.*

Section III

TEST INSTRUMENTS

ELECTRICAL TEST EQUIPMENT

There are four factors in an electrical circuit:

Volts, a measurement of electrical pressure or force

Amperes, a measurement of the rate of electron flow

Ohms, a measurement of resistance to electron flow

Watts, a measurement of electrical power

A test instrument or meter is used to measure each of these factors. These meters can measure one or more of four functions and are available in all price ranges.

Meter movements are delicate instruments and must be handled with care. Extreme temperature or humidity changes, or rough handling, can destroy your most useful test equipment.

A safety warning accompanying the Simpson 260 volt•ohm•milliammeter reads:

This instrument is designed to prevent accidental shock to the operator when properly used. However, no engineering design can render safe an instrument that is used carelessly.

A. Do not work alone when making measurements of circuits where a shock hazard can exist. Notify another person that you intend to make such a measurement.

B. Locate all voltage sources and accessible paths prior to making measurement connections. Check that the equipment is properly grounded and the right rating and type of fuse(s) is installed. Set the instrument to the proper range before power is applied.

C. Remember, voltages may appear unexpectedly in defective equipment. An open bleeder resistor may result in a capacitor retaining a dangerous charge. Turn off power and discharge all capacitors before connecting or disconnecting test leads to and from the circuit being measured.

D. For your own safety, inspect the test leads for cracks, breaks, or crazes in the insulation, probes, and connectors before each use. If any defects exist, replace the test leads immediately.

E. Do not make measurements in a circuit where corona is present. Corona can be identified by a pale-blue color emanating from sharp metal points in the circuit, the odor of ozone, and its sound.

F. Hands, shoes, floor, and workbench must be dry. Avoid making measurements under humid, damp, or other environmental conditions that could affect the dielectric withstanding voltage of the test leads or instrument.

G. For maximum safety, do not touch test leads or instrument while power is applied to the circuit being measured.

H. Use extreme caution when making measurements in a radio frequency (RF) circuit where a dangerous combination of voltages could be present, such as in a modulated RF amplifier.

I. Do not make measurements using test leads which differ from those originally furnished with the instrument.

J. Do not come into contact with any object which could provide a currrent path to the common side of the circuit under test or power line ground. Always stand on a dry insulating surface capable of withstanding the voltage being measured or that could be encountered.

K. The range or function switch should only be changed when the power to the circuit under measurement is turned off. This will provide maximum safety to the user, eliminate arcing at the switch contacts and prolong the life of the instrument.

Because the voltmeter is used to determine the presence of voltage, a potential danger to the user may exist. These precautions should be applied to the use of all test equipment that is used on a circuit with the main power supply on.

YOU NEED NOT FEAR ELECTRICITY BUT YOU SHOULD RESPECT IT

THE VOLTMETER

Voltage is usually described as the force or pressure necessary to make the electrons flow. The voltmeter is the instrument used to measure the voltage, Figure 3-1.

When using the voltmeter to trace circuits, the voltmeter is always parallel to the circuit. When using the voltmeter, we are looking for one of four readings.

1. No voltage across switch contacts indicates that the contacts are closed, Figure 3-2a.

2. A voltage reading across switch contacts indicates that the contacts are open, Figure 3-2b.

3. No voltage at the terminals of a motor or coil indicates that there is no voltage available to the motor or coil, Figure 3-2c.

4. A voltage reading at the terminals of a motor or coil indicates that voltage is available. If the motor or coil does not operate, then they are defective, Figure 3-2d.

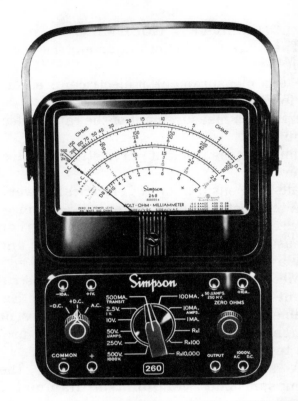

FIG. 3-1. Simpson 260® Volt•Ohm•Milliammeter. *Courtesy Simpson Electric Co.*

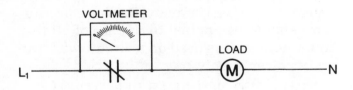

FIG. 3-2a. No voltage indicates that the contacts are closed.

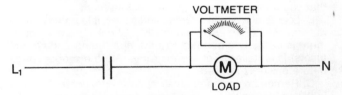

FIG. 3-2c. No voltage indicates that there is no voltage available to the motor.

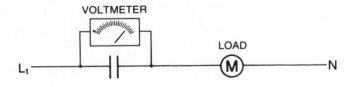

FIG. 3-2b. Voltage indicates that the contacts are open.

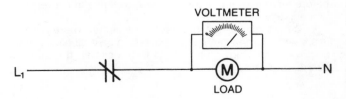

FIG. 3-2d. Voltage indicates that there is voltage available to the motor.

AMMETERS

The ampere, which is the rate of flow of electrons or current, is measured with an amp meter or ammeter, Figure 3-3. The ammeter must be connected in series with the load which can be time consuming.

A quicker method is to use a clamp-on ammeter, sometimes called an Amprobe, Figure 3-4, to surround a single conductor and thus read the amperage.

The Amprobe will quickly read the current draw of an electrical load, Figure 3-5. A current draw that is 10% above or below rated amperage is permissible. Greater variations than 10% indicate that a problem is developing or has already developed.

FIG. 3-4. Amprobe Volt•Amp•Ohmmeter. *Courtesy Amprobe Instrument.*

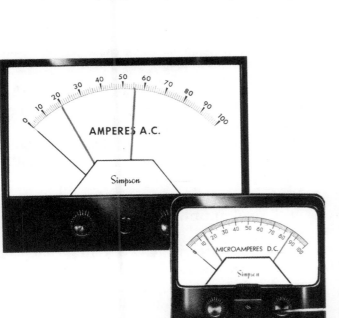

FIG. 3-3. Ammeter. *Courtesy Simpson Electric Co.*

FIG. 3-5. Using an Amprobe to determine the current draw of an electric motor.

THE OHMMETER

Resistance to electron flow is present is all conductors and is measured in ohms.

WARNING: The ohmmeter can only be used when the power supply is disconnected. The ohmmeter operates from a battery within the instrument rather than using line voltage.

The ohmmeter can be used to test capacitors, find common, run and start in a single phase compressor motor, and as a continuity tester for checking fuses, Figure 3-6.

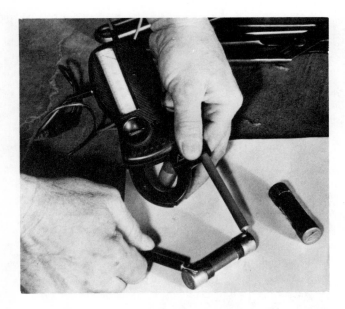

FIG. 3-6. Using an Amprobe as an ohmmeter to check fuses.

Testing AC Capacitors

WARNING: Always discharge capacitors before making any test and before removing the the capacitor from the circuit. A fully charged capacitor could cause a burn if discharged through your body.

One method used for quick testing on the job is the ohmmeter test. First, set the meter to the highest range.

1. If the capacitor is shorted, there will be a low resistance reading. The meter needle could move to zero.

2. If the capacitor is open, the resistance will read infinity. The needle will not move.

3. If the capacitor is good (having some capacitance), the needle will deflect rapidly while the capacitor charges itself from the battery in the ohmmeter. The needle will then drift slowly back to infinity as the charge bleeds away.

The capacitor must be discharged each time this test is performed.

The ohmmeter test is not conclusive, but will indicate whether the capacitor is shorted or open or not shorted nor open. The test does not detect a weak capacitor.

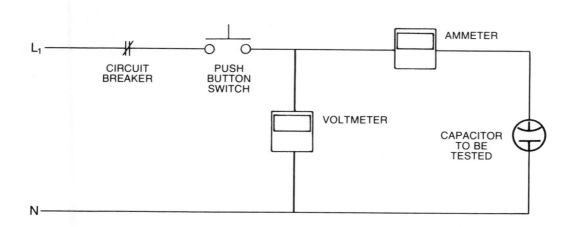

FIG. 3-7. Testing a capacitor with a voltmeter and an ammeter that have been wired together.

Several companies have developed test equipment to accurately measure capacitance or mfd. The tester consists of an ac voltmeter and an ac ammeter wired together as shown in Figure 3-7. With the capacitor in the test circuit:

1. Test the capacitor for not more than 10 seconds.
2. Note both the ammeter and voltmeter readings.
3. Calculate the capacity using this formula

$$\frac{2650 \times \text{amps}}{\text{volts}} = \text{MFD}$$

This method will give a good approximation of capacity, within $\pm10\%$.

1. If capacity is much lower than rated mfd, the capacitor is weak and overage.
2, If capacity is much higher than rated mfd, the capacitor is probably developing an internal short.

Remember that capacitors are affected by temperature. All tests must be conducted at 25°C (77°F). A capacitor that is too hot or too cold will not give accurate test results.

Identifying Motor Terminals

If motor terminal markings are illegible, use the ohmmeter to measure the resistance between the three terminals that you have labeled 1, 2 and 3. You might find that the resistance between 1 and 2 is 5 ohms, between 2 and 3 is 15 ohms and between 1 and 3 is 20 ohms. The highest reading indicates that you have measured the resistance of both the start and run windings in series. Therefore, 1 and 3 are obviously run and start and 2 is common. Since you know that the start winding has the higher resistance, 3 is start and 1 is run.

Section IV

CREATING ELECTRICAL SCHEMATICS

L₁   N

```
 1  |.......................................................................| 1
 2  |.......................................................................| 2
 3  |.......................................................................| 3
 4  |.......................................................................| 4
 5  |.......................................................................| 5
 6  |.......................................................................| 6
 7  |.......................................................................| 7
 8  |.......................................................................| 8
 9  |.......................................................................| 9
10  |.......................................................................| 10
11  |.......................................................................| 11
12  |.......................................................................| 12
13  |.......................................................................| 13
14  |.......................................................................| 14
15  |.......................................................................| 15
16  |.......................................................................| 16
17  |.......................................................................| 17
18  |.......................................................................| 18
19  |.......................................................................| 19
20  |.......................................................................| 20
21  |.......................................................................| 21
22  |.......................................................................| 22
23  |.......................................................................| 23
24  |.......................................................................| 24
25  |.......................................................................| 25
```

THE SCHEMATIC LAYOUT SHEET

The schematic layout sheet will be used for all 10 examples in this section. The vertical line at the left, L_1, is the hot line, usually 115v, 60 cycle (60 Hz), single phase (1ϕ), alternating current (ac). The vertical line at the right, N, is the neutral or return line. The horizontal lines, numbered 1 through 25, are reserved for a number of parallel circuits between L_1 and N.

The examples themselves will start with very simple circuits and progress to rather complex electrical systems. They are designed to give you increasing confidence in your ability to understand and work with a wide range of common electrical circuits.

Before the electrical schematic can be drawn, you must first do three things.

1. DEFINE THE FUNCTION OF THE EQUIPMENT

Ask yourself: what is this equipment and its circuits designed to do? The function of the basic forced air furnace is to generate heat for your personal comfort. The essential components are a source of heat and a fan to distribute air. Do you want uniform comfort? Of course you do, so you control the fan with a plenum switch. Do you want to regulate the heat automatically? Of course you do, so you add a thermostat. Now the function of the furnace has to be redefined, based on your additional requirements. Your furnace is no longer merely a means to generate heat, it is now a means to uniformly and automatically generate and distribute heat. Go one step further: add a little more equipment and two more electrical circuits and this same furnace will both heat and cool, to give you year-round personal comfort.

This is the way you must define the function of the equipment because function determines the components to be used in your next step.

2. LIST THE ELECTRICAL COMPONENTS

Section II gave you a brief description of some of the controls you will be employing in these examples. How do you know which ones to use?

Following Step 1, review the function of the equipment: in this case, an automatically and uniformly controlled, gas-fired, forced air heating and cooling system operating on a standard, domestic power supply with low voltage controls.

Based on this definition, here are the components and sources you need:

Standard domestic power	*115v, 60 Hz, 1ϕ, ac*
Gas-fired	*Gas valve*
Forced air	*Fan motor*
Uniform comfort	*Plenum switch*
Automatic heating and cooling	*Heating and cooling thermostat*
Low voltage control	*Transformer*
Cooling	*Compressor and relay*

3. GO STEP-BY-STEP THROUGH THE ELECTRICAL SEQUENCE

In other words, ask yourself, "What happens next?"

Right now, if you were asked, "How do you get cold air?" you would probably reply, "You turn down the thermostat until the fan goes on. Then, you get cold air."

Later, when you have mastered the schematic, you will know that the process of producing cold air requires not one, but a number of steps in sequence. And, you will know that one step is separated from the other by a microsecond time interval, even though the entire sequence seems to occur instantly.

Let's apply this 3-step approach to our first example, an air-conditioning compressor.

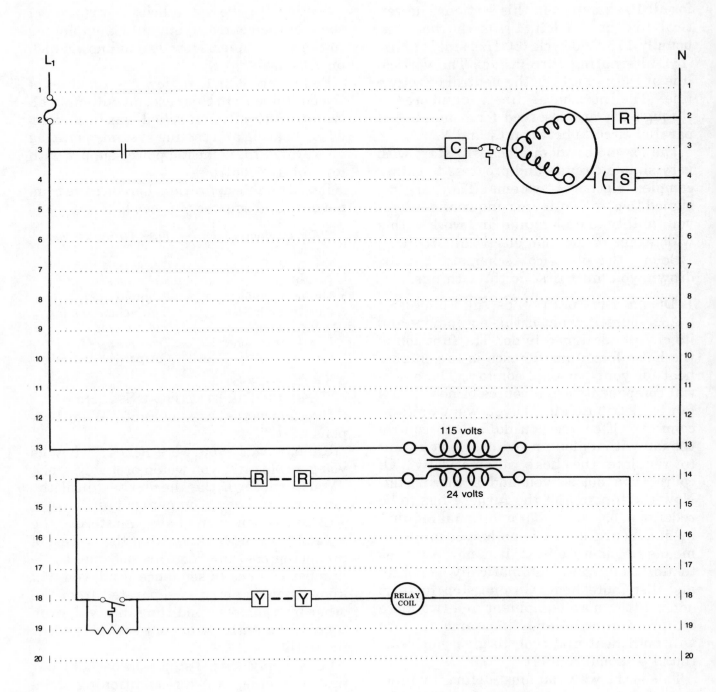

EXAMPLE 1
AIR CONDITIONING COMPRESSOR

1. DEFINE THE FUNCTION OF THE EQUIPMENT

This is an internally-protected compressor, automatically operated by a low voltage thermostat, from a 115v source.

2. LIST THE ELECTRICAL COMPONENTS

- The standard electrical source is 115v, 60 cycle (60 Hz), single phase (1φ), alternating current (ac).
- A fuse ⌇ is required by the Safety Code.
- The internal protector ⌇ is a standard feature of all compressors. Actually it is wired inside the shell of a hermetically-sealed compressor. Schematically, it is shown in series with the common leg of the two-circuit compressor motor.
- The compressor may have one of a number of starting circuits. In this example, the compressor employs a permanent split capacitor ⌇ (PSC) motor and has a run capacitor ⌇S in the motor starting circuit. The use of a PSC motor tells you that the compressor requires low starting torque.
- A contactor ⌇ is used to start the compressor and is wired in series with the internal protector. The coil for the contactor ⌇ is wired into the 24v circuit.
- A step-down transformer (from 115v to 24v) ⌇ is required for the low-voltage circuit.
- A cooling thermostat ⌇, operating on 24v, is required for the control circuit. Field wiring ——— from the thermostat to the compressor contactor coil will be required. Terminal R on the thermostat is connected to terminal R on the transformer. Terminal Y on the thermostat is connected to Y on the contactor.

3. GO STEP-BY-STEP THROUGH THE ELECTRICAL SEQUENCE

- Line power must be supplied to the high (115v) side of the transformer ⌇.
- When the thermostat ⌇ closes, on a temperature rise, the circuit is completed between terminals R and Y.
- This induces a 24v current in the low side of the transformer and energizes the compressor contactor coil ⌇.
- The normally open contacts ⌇, in the 115v circuit, close ⌇ to supply current, through the internal protector ⌇, to the compressor motor ⌇.
- Current flows through both the start and run windings to the neutral line, N. When the motor attains approximately 80% of its normal running speed, the start winding drops out and the motor continues to operate on the run winding only.

4. DRAW THE SCHEMATIC

Using the layout sheet:

Step 1. Insert a fuse ⸮ in L_1 between lines 1 and 2.

STEP 2. Draw the transformer ⸜⸝⸜⸝ between lines 13 and 14 and connect the 115v side of the transformer to L_1 and N along line 13.

STEP 3. On line 14, draw terminal Ⓡ and connect it, with low voltage field wiring ———, to another terminal Ⓡ on the 24v side of the transformer. Connect the transformer to Ⓡ.

STEP 4. On line 18, draw terminal Ⓨ and connect it, with field wiring ———, to another terminal Ⓨ. Draw a contactor coil ⓇⒺⓁⒶⓎ and connect it to Ⓨ and the 24v side of the transformer.

STEP 5. On line 18, draw a normally-open thermostat ⸜ and connect it to terminals Ⓡ and Ⓨ.

STEP 6. On line 19, draw a resistor ⟋⟍⟋⟍ and connect it to line 18 to create a parallel circuit with the thermostat. This is the cooling anticipator.

STEP 7. On line 3, connect the contactor contacts ┤├ to L_1. Connect the contacts to the common lead Ⓒ of the compressor motor. Position the internal protector ⸜ between Ⓒ and the junction of the start and run windings to indicate that that it is an integral part of the common lead to the motor.

STEP 8. Connect the run winding to N along line 2. Connect the motor start winding to the run capacitor ┤├Ⓢ on line 4 and the ground side of the capacitor to line N.

STEP 9. Close the thermostat switch between terminals Ⓡ and Ⓨ and draw a slash through the contactor ⫽, indicating that the normally open contacts have been closed by the contactor coil. The compressor is now in normal operation.

L₁   N

| |
1 |. . . . . | 1

2 |. . . . . | 2

3 |. . . . . | 3

4 |. . . . . | 4

5 |. . . . . | 5

6 |. . . . . | 6

7 |. . . . . | 7

8 |. . . . . | 8

9 |. . . . . | 9

10 |. . . . . | 10

11 |. . . . . | 11

12 |. . . . . | 12

13 |. . . . . | 13

14 |. . . . . | 14

15 |. . . . . | 15

16 |. . . . . | 16

17 |. . . . . | 17

18 |. . . . . | 18

19 |. . . . . | 19

20 |. . . . . | 20

L₁   N

STEP 1

STEP 2

STEP 3

STEP 4

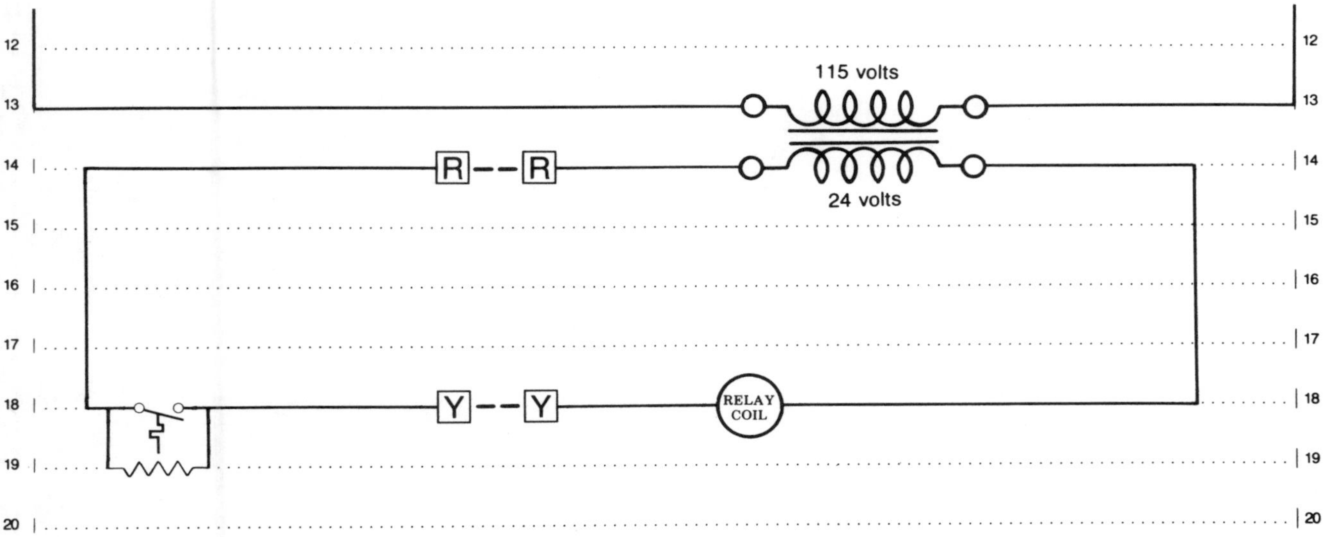

STEPS 5 AND 6

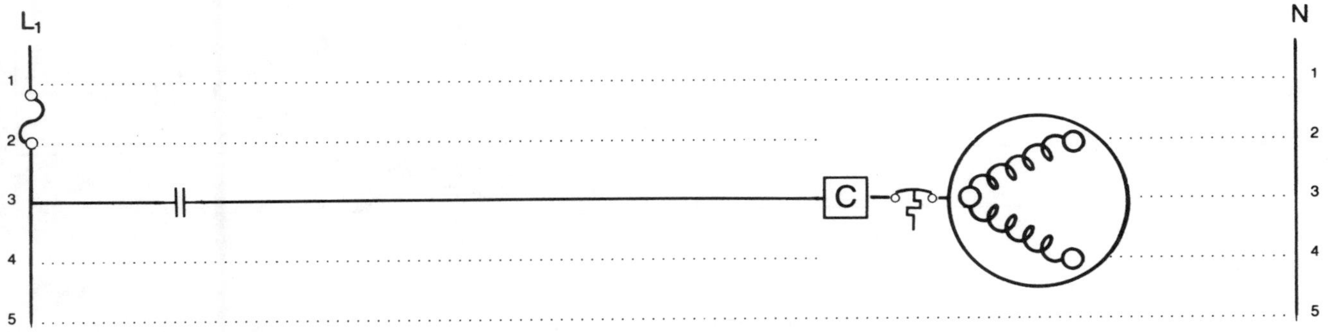

STEP 7

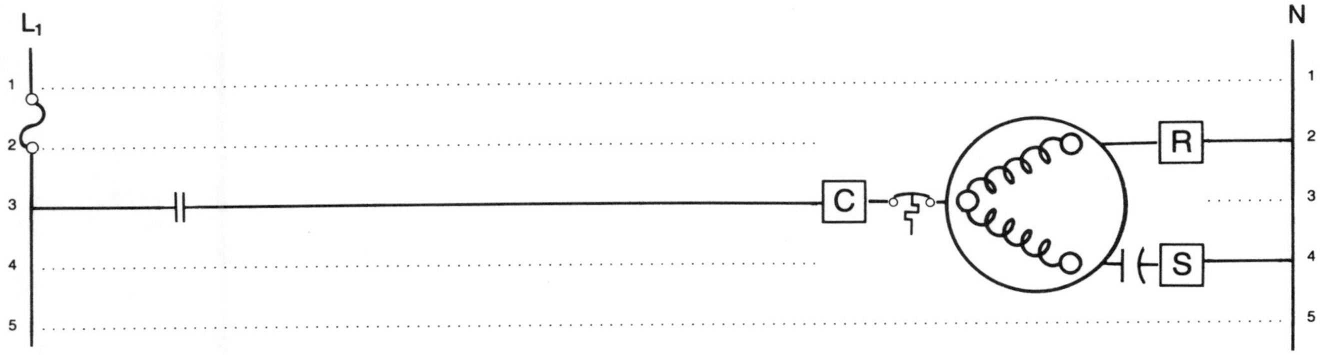

STEP 8

L₁   N

115 volts

24 volts

EXAMPLE 2
GAS-FIRED, FORCED AIR FURNACE

The furnace system used in this example is typical of that installed in many homes. The furnace is delivered as a complete system, lacking only the remote thermostat.

1. DEFINE THE FUNCTION OF THE EQUIPMENT

This is a gas-fired, forced air furnace, operating on line voltage, with automatic, low voltage controls. Provision is made for uniform air delivery temperatures and a safety control prevents furnace overheating.

2. LIST THE ELECTRICAL COMPONENTS
- The standard home electrical source is 115v, 60 cycle (60 Hz), single phase (1φ), alternating current (ac).
- A fuse ⌇ is required by the Safety Code.
- A step-down transformer ⁓⁓ᴍ⁓ is required for low (24v) voltage.
- A thermostat ⊤°, with terminals [R] and [W], is required for automatic control.
- A gas valve ⊘ is required for heat generation.
- A normally-closed thermal limit switch ⊤° is needed to prevent overheating.
- An internally-protected, permanent split capacitor (PSC) fan motor ⊶◉⊷ is needed to drive the fan.
- A normally open thermal plenum switch ⊤° is needed for air temperature control.

3. GO STEP-BY-STEP THROUGH THE ELECTRICAL SEQUENCE
- Line voltage (115v ac) must be supplied to the high side of the transformer ⁓⁓ᴍ⁓.
- When the thermostat ⊤° closes, on a temperature fall, the circuit is completed between terminals [R] and [W].
- This induces a 24v currrent in the low side of the transformer and energizes the gas valve ⊘ if the thermal limit switch is closed, as is normal.
- The gas valve can now generate heat and will continue to do so until the plenum overheats at approximately 180°F. At this temperature, the thermal limit switch ⊤° will open, and remain open, until the plenum temperature drops to 110 to 120°F. In the meanwhile, the gas valve is off. Until the fan ⊶◉⊷ is in operation, the gas valve will be cycled on and off by the thermal limit switch.
- Fan motor operation is controlled by the normally open plenum switch ⊤° which activates the fan motor when the plenum temperature reaches 140 to 150°F. Were the fan to operate when the gas valve goes on, the fan would deliver an uncomfortable stream of unheated air on start-up and leave unused heat in the plenum on shut-down. Instead, the fan continues to operate, even with the gas valve off, until the plenum temperature drops below 120°F and opens the plenum switch.

4. DRAW THE SCHEMATIC

STEP 1. Insert a fuse ⌇ in L₁ between line 1 and line 2.

STEP 2. Draw a transformer ⌇ between lines 13 and 14 and connect the 115v side of the transformer to L₁ and N along line 13.

STEP 3. On line 14, draw terminal Ⓡ and connect it, with low voltage field wiring ———, to another terminal Ⓡ on the 24v side of the transformer. Connect the transformer to Ⓡ.

STEP 4. On line 16, draw terminal Ⓦ and connect it, with field wiring ———, to another terminal Ⓦ.

STEP 5. Draw a gas valve ⊙ on line 16 and connect it to terminal Ⓦ. Connect the normally closed thermal limit switch in series with the gas valve and the 24v side of the transformer.

STEP 6. On line 16, draw a normally closed thermostat switch in series with a variable resistor which is the heat anticipator. Connect these elements to Ⓡ and Ⓦ.

STEP 7. Close the thermostat. The gas valve ⊙ will operate, and generate heat, until . . .

STEP 8. The thermal limit switch opens the circuit to the gas valve. (As long as the thermostat remains closed, the system will alternate between STEPS 7 and 8.)

STEP 9. On line 11, draw the normally closed internal protector between terminal Ⓒ and the junction of the start and run windings. Connect the run winding to N along line 10. Insert a capacitor ⊣⊢Ⓢ between the start winding and terminal Ⓢ. Connect Ⓢ to N along line 12.

STEP 10. On line 11, connect a normally open plenum switch to L₁ and terminal Ⓒ.

STEP 11. Close the thermostat to start the gas valve ⊙. Wait one minute, to allow heat to reach the plenum switch. When the heat operated plenum switch closes, the system is in normal operation.

STEP 12. Open the thermostat. The plenum switch will remain closed, and the fan will continue to operate, until the plenum cools down. The plenum switch will then open and the system will be on standby.

L₁   N

1 | .... | 1

2 | .... | 2

3 | .... | 3

4 | .... | 4

5 | .... | 5

6 | .... | 6

7 | .... | 7

8 | .... | 8

9 | .... | 9

10 | .... | 10

11 | .... | 11

12 | .... | 12

13 | .... | 13

14 | .... | 14

15 | .... | 15

16 | .... | 16

17 | .... | 17

18 | .... | 18

19 | .... | 19

20 | .... | 20

L1
N
1
2
3
1
2
3

STEP 1

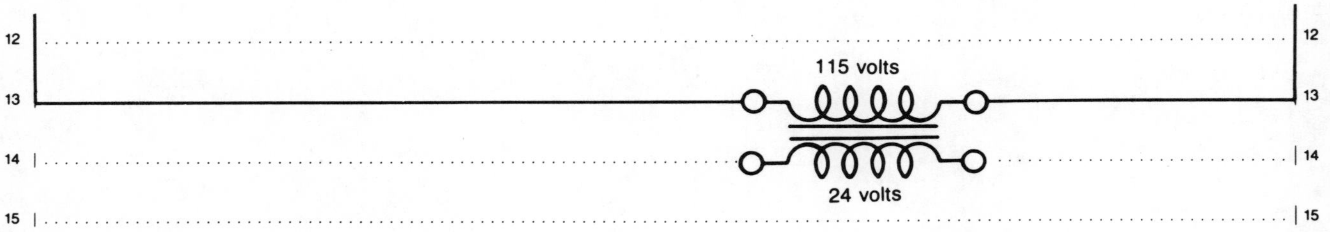
12
13
14
15
115 volts
24 volts
12
13
14
15

STEP 2

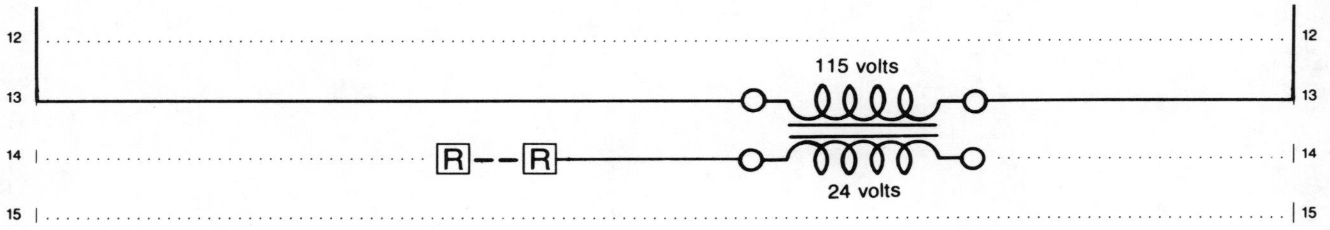
12
13
14
15
115 volts
R--R
24 volts
12
13
14
15

STEP 3

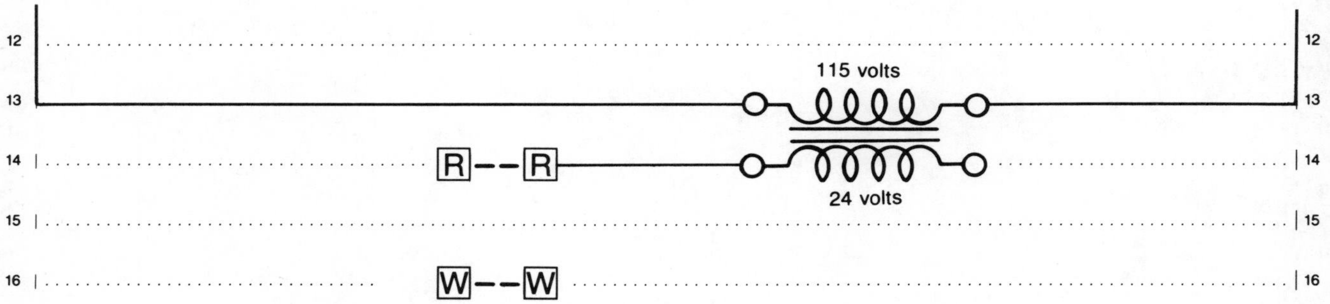
12
13
14
15
16
115 volts
R--R
24 volts
W--W
12
13
14
15
16

STEP 4

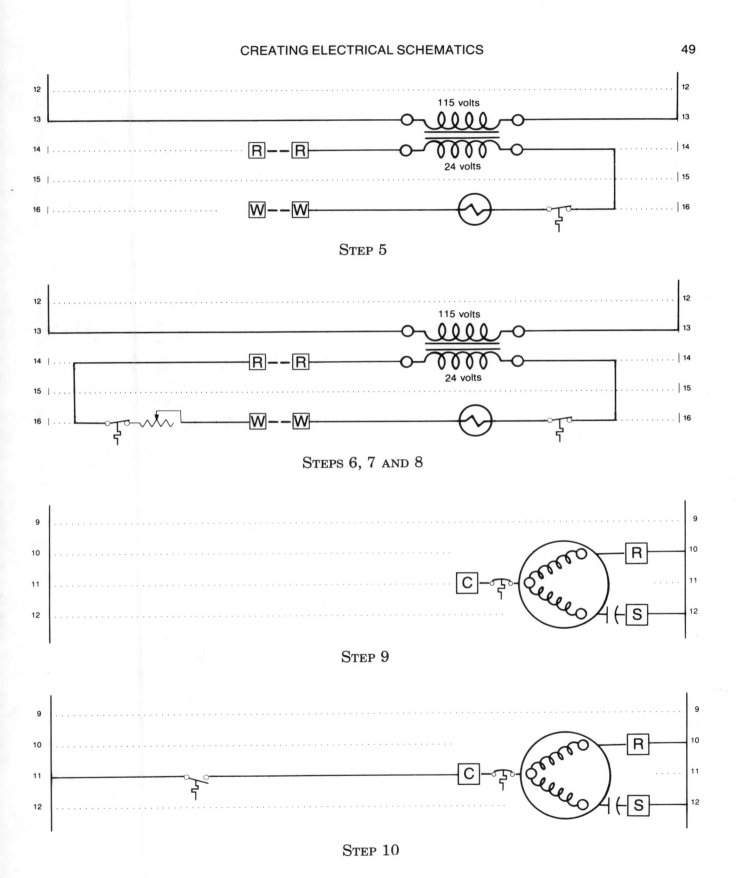

STEP 5

STEPS 6, 7 AND 8

STEP 9

STEP 10

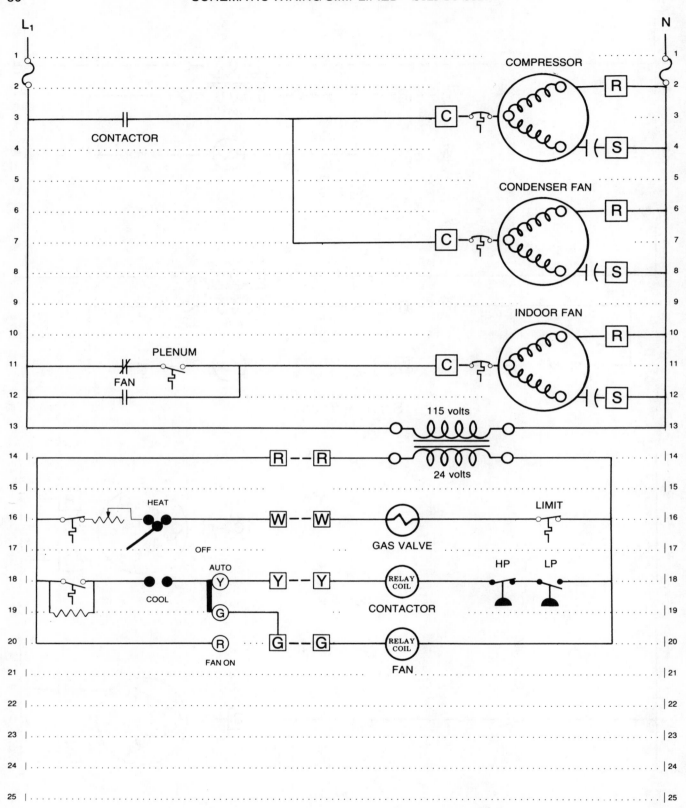

EXAMPLE 3
GAS-FIRED, FORCED AIR FURNACE WITH AUTOMATIC AIR CONDITIONING

All of the controls shown in this heating/cooling combination are prewired at the factory, with the exception of the thermostat which is furnished by the installer. For simplicity's sake, field wiring between the furnace and the outside-mounted compressor/condenser unit will not be indicated.

1. DEFINE THE FUNCTION OF THE EQUIPMENT

This is a gas-fired, forced air furnace and air conditioner, operating on line voltage, with automatic, low voltage, controls.

The heating side of this combination is designed to provide uniform air delivery temperatures and has a safety control to prevent overheating.

On the cooling side, the compressor is protected by high pressure and low pressure cut-outs.

A forced-air fan operates when either heating or cooling is called for and, as an added feature, can be operated continuously while either system is on standby.

2. LIST THE ELECTRICAL COMPONENTS

- The standard home electrical source is 115v, 60 cycle (60 Hz), single phase (1φ), alternating current (ac).
- A fuse ⌇ is required by the Safety Code.
- A step-down transformer ⌁ is required for low (24v) voltage.
- A heating/cooling thermostat with terminals �R (common), W (heat), Y (cooling), and G (fan), is required for automatic control.
- A gas valve ⊘ is required for heat generation.
- A normally-closed thermal limit switch ⌁ is needed to prevent overheating.
- An internally-protected, permanent split capacitor fan motor ⌁ (PSC) is needed to drive the forced-air fan.
- A normally open, thermal plenum switch ⌁ is needed for air temperature control.
- A high pressure �⊤ and low pressure �⊥ cut-out are needed to protect the compressor.
- A contactor relay with a coil (RELAY COIL) and a set of contacts ⊣⊢ is needed to start the compressor and condenser fan motors.
- A fan relay with a coil (RELAY COIL), and one set of normally closed ⊣⊬ and one set of normally open ⊣⊢ contacts, is needed to permit continuous fan operation.
- An internally-protected, permanent split capacitor compressor motor and condenser fan motor ⌁ are both needed for cooling.

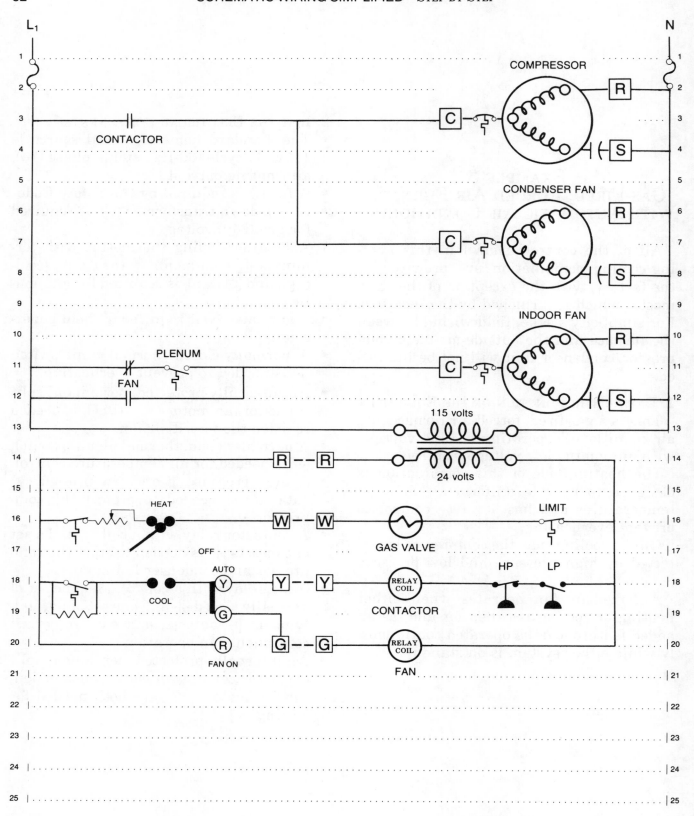

3. GO STEP-BY-STEP THROUGH THE ELECTRICAL SEQUENCE

HEATING

- Line voltage (115v) must be supplied to the high side of the transformer ⌇⌇⌇.
- When heating is desired, the manual mode switch on the thermostat must be set on **Heat** and the manual fan control switch is usually on **Auto**. When the heating thermostat closes on a temperature fall, a circuit is completed between terminals [R] and [W]. This completes a circuit through the low (24v) side of the transformer to the gas valve ⊙ and normally-closed thermal limit switch, to start the heating cycle. When the temperature in the plenum reaches 140° to 150°F, the normally open fan switch closes to complete a line voltage circuit through the normally closed side ─╫─ of the indoor fan relay to the indoor fan motor.

COOLING

- When cooling is desired, the manual mode switch on the thermostat must be set on **Cool**. The manual fan control switch is usually on **Auto**. When the cooling thermostat closes on a temperature rise, a circuit is completed between terminals [R] and [Y]. This completes a circuit through the low side of the transformer to the contactor coil (RELAY COIL) and through the normally closed high pressure and low pressure cut-outs. The contactor coil closes the contacts ─╫─ and completes parallel circuits to the start winding of the compressor and condenser fan motors. At the same time, another circuit is completed from [R] to [G] through the indoor fan relay coil (RELAY COIL). When the coil is energized, it opens the normally closed set of contacts ─╫─ and closes the normally open set of contacts ─╫─. As a result, the normally open fan switch is bypassed and a circuit is completed to the start winding of the indoor fan motor.
- When continuous fan operation is required, the manual fan switch is moved to **On**. This will complete a circuit from [R] to [G] and energize the indoor fan relay coil (RELAY COIL). With the plenum switch bypassed through the indoor fan relay ─╫─, the fan will operate continuously, even though neither heating nor cooling is called for and will continue to operate when either heating or cooling are desired.

DRAW THE SCHEMATIC

STEP 1. Insert a fuse ⌇ between line 1 and line 2.

STEP 2. Draw a step-down transformer ⌁⌁ between lines 13 and 14 and connect the 115v side to L₁ and N along line 13.

STEP 3. Draw four pairs of field wired ——— terminals, R R on line 14, W W on line 16, Y Y on line 18, and G G on line 20.

STEP 4. On line 14, connect terminal R to the 24v side of the transformer.

STEP 5. On line 16, draw a normally-closed temperature actuated switch (the heating thermostat) in series with a variable resistor (the heat anticipator). Join the heat anticipator to a pair of open contact buttons ● ● and connect the buttons to terminal W on the thermostat. Continuing on line 16, connect a gas valve ⊘ between terminal W and a normally-closed, temperature actuated limit switch. Link the limit switch to the return side of the transformer on line 14.

STEP 6. On line 18, draw a normally open, temperature actuated switch (the cooling thermostat) and connect it to a pair of open contact buttons. Connect the buttons to terminal Y on the thermostat. Continuing on line 18, connect the contactor coil to its terminal Y and to a pair of normally-closed high and normally-open low pressure switches. Link the pressure switches to the return side of the transformer on line 14.

STEP 7. On line 19, draw a variable resistor ∿∿∿ (the cooling anticipator) and wire it parallel with the cooling thermostat by connecting it to line 18.

STEP 8. Close the gap between the two contact buttons ● ● on line 16 with a third button ● attached to an arm that pivots from line 17. This arm is the heat/cool selector switch which can close the gap between the two buttons on line 16, to complete the heating circuit and isolate the cooling circuit, or close the gap between the two buttons on line 18, to complete the cooling circuit and isolate the heating circuit.

STEP 9. On line 20, connect a fan relay between its terminal G and the return side of the transformer.

STEP 10. Draw the internal fan contacts by inserting terminal Ⓨ on line 18, terminal Ⓖ on line 19, and terminal Ⓡ on line 20. Connect terminal Ⓖ to terminal G on line 20. Connect terminal Ⓡ and the two thermostat switches to terminal R on line 14.

Connect terminal Ⓨ to terminal Ⓖ with a sliding bar |. With the bar in the up or Auto position, joining Ⓨ and Ⓖ, the fan relay is controlled by the thermostat. With the bar in the down, or Fan On position, joining Ⓖ and Ⓡ, the fan runs constantly, regardless of the thermostat action. This completes the low voltage circuits.

L₁   N
| |
1 | . . . . | 1

2 | . . . . | 2

3 | . . . . | 3

4 | . . . . | 4

5 | . . . . | 5

6 | . . . . | 6

7 | . . . . | 7

8 | . . . . | 8

9 | . . . . | 9

10 | . . . . | 10

11 | . . . . | 11

12 | . . . . | 12

13 | . . . . | 13

14 | . . . . | 14

15 | . . . . | 15

16 | . . . . | 16

17 | . . . . | 17

18 | . . . . | 18

19 | . . . . | 19

20 | . . . . | 20

21 | . . . . | 21

22 | . . . . | 22

23 | . . . . | 23

24 | . . . . | 24

25 | . . . . | 25

STEP 11. Draw three internally protected PSC motors ⊣◯⊢ with their common C terminals on lines 3, 7, and 11. Connect the run R and start S terminals to N.

STEP 12. Draw the contactor contacts ⊣⊢ for the compressor motor on line 3 and connect them to L₁ and terminal C of the compressor.

STEP 13. On line 7, connect terminal C of the condenser fan to the compressor on line 3.

STEP 14. On line 11, draw a pair of normally closed fan contacts ⊣/⊢ and a normally open plenum switch and join them to the C terminal of the indoor fan motor and L₁.

STEP 15. On line 12, draw in the normally open set of indoor fan relay contacts ⊣⊢. Wire them from L₁ to the fan motor, bypassing the plenum fan switch.

STEP 16. Recheck the low voltage circuits to determine how the compressor and compressor fan are started simultaneously, how the internal fan operates on Heat and on Cool, and how the internal fan motor is operated when neither heating nor cooling is called for.

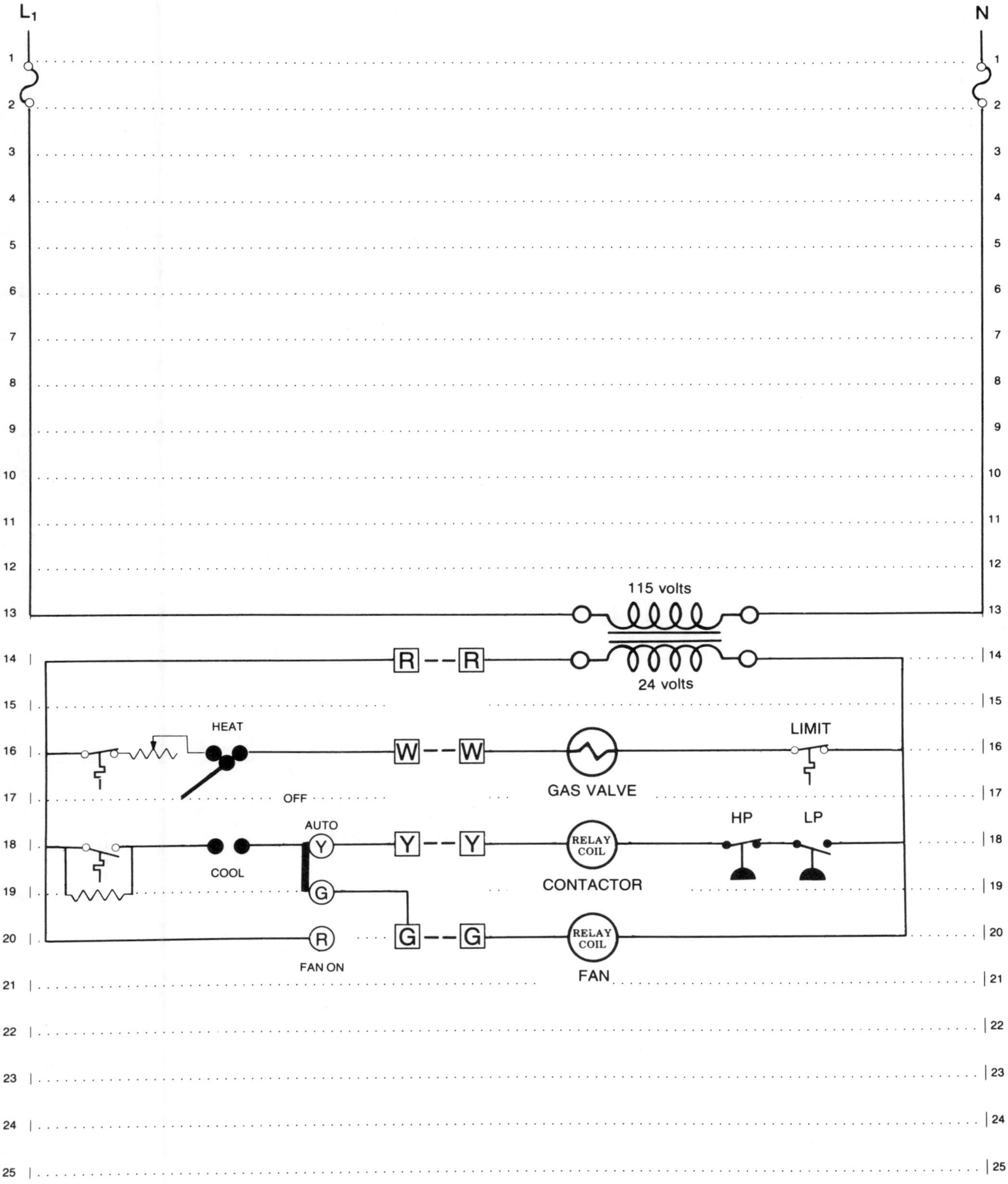

L₁ N

1 1
2 2
3 3
4 4
5 5
6 6
7 7
8 8
9 9
10 10
11 11
12 12

115 volts
13 13

R - R 24 volts
14 14

15 15

HEAT LIMIT
16 16

OFF GAS VALVE
17 17

AUTO HP LP
18 Y Y - Y RELAY COIL 18
COOL
19 CONTACTOR 19

20 R G - G RELAY COIL 20

FAN ON FAN
21 21

22 22

23 23

24 24

25 25

L₁   N

1

2

3

Step 1

115 volts

13   13

14   R--R   24 volts   14

15   15

16   W--W   16

17   17

18   Y--Y   18

19   19

20   G--G   20

Steps 2, 3 and 4

115 volts

13   13

14   R--R   24 volts   14

15   15

LIMIT

16   W--W   GAS VALVE   16

17   17

18   Y--Y   18

19   19

20   G--G   20

Step 5

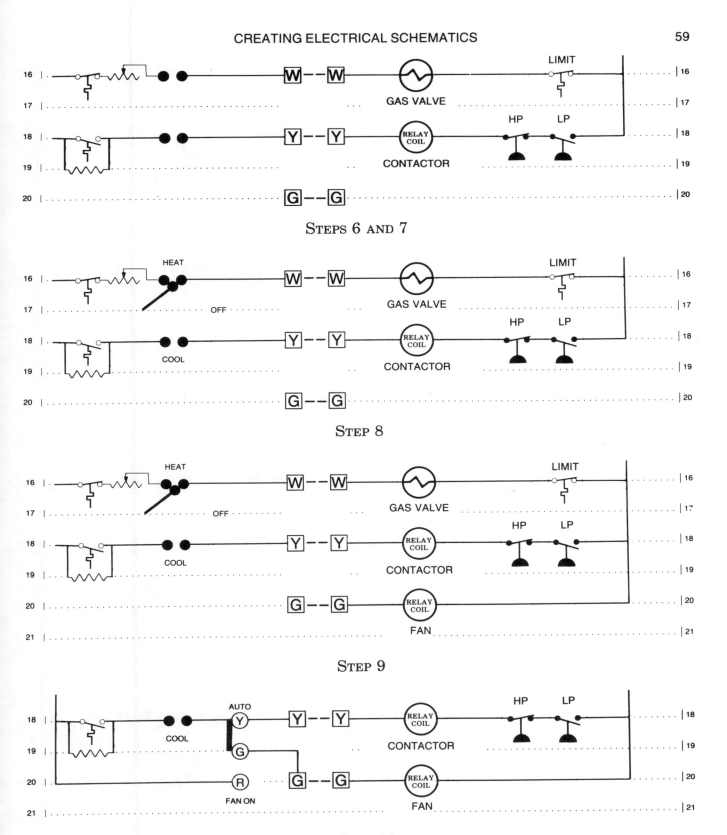

STEPS 6 AND 7

STEP 8

STEP 9

STEP 10

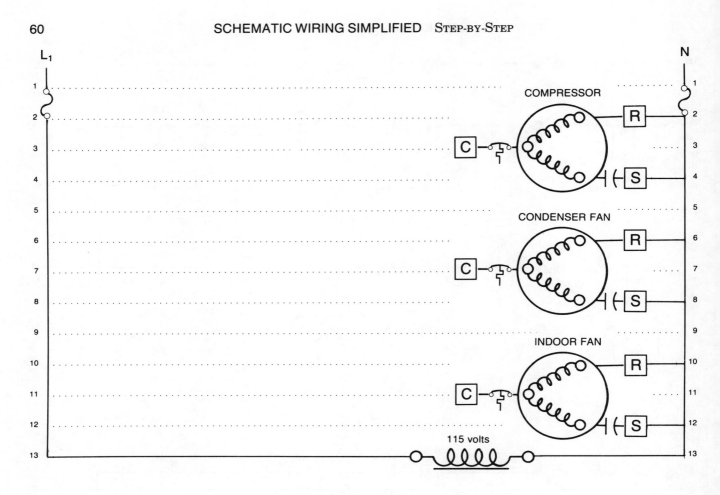

STEP 11

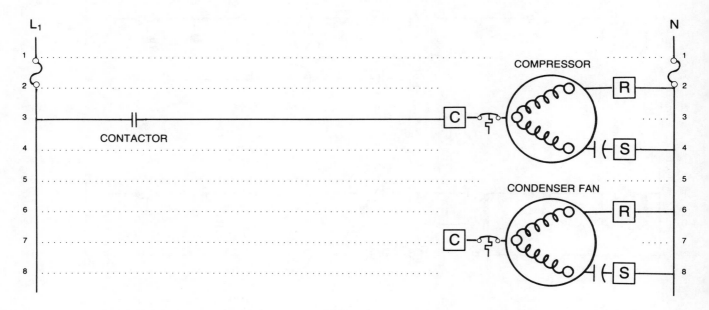

STEP 12

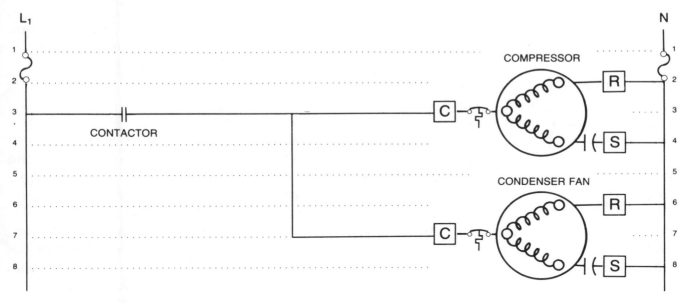

STEP 13

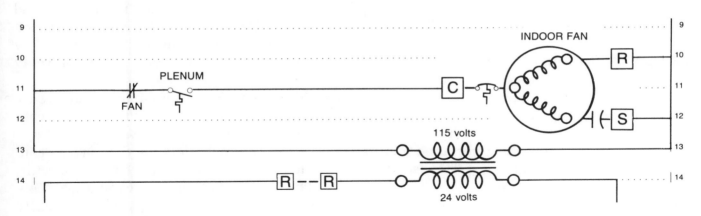

STEP 14

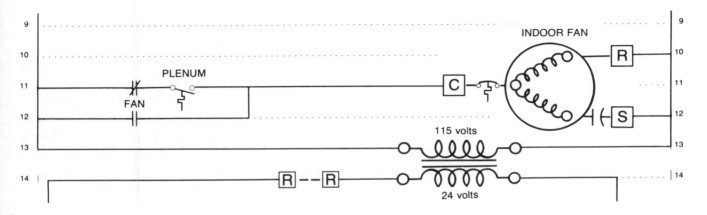

STEP 15

EXAMPLE 4
OIL-FIRED, FORCED AIR FURNACE

This oil heating system uses the same air temperature controls as a gas-fired system. What is unique is a burner primary control that incorporates a number of safety features to shut down the oil delivery system in the event of ignition failure or termination. The primary control is an encapsulated unit that cannot be repaired. However, its components will be reviewed in order to understand the operation of the safety features.

1. DEFINE THE FUNCTION OF THE EQUIPMENT

This is an oil-fired, forced air furnace requiring a low voltage thermostat and having air delivery temperature controls and burner ignition controls as safety features.

2. LIST THE ELECTRICAL COMPONENTS
- The standard home electrical source is 115v, 60 cycle (60 Hz), single phase (1φ), alternating current (ac).
- A fuse ⌇ is required by the Safety Code.
- An internally-protected, permanent split capacitor fan motor ⊝⁷⊕ᴴ⊟ is needed to drive the forced-air fan.
- A normally-open plenum switch ⊤ is needed for air temperature control.
- A normally-closed thermal limit switch ⊤ is needed to prevent overheating.
- A burner motor relay (RELAY COIL) is needed to control the motor (PUMP MOTOR) that both pumps the oil and supplies combustion air.
- A 10,000v ignition transformer ⌇⌇ and electrodes ⌐⌐ are needed to ignite the oil.
- A cad cell flame detector ⊙ is needed to assure shutdown on flame-out.
- An oil burner primary control is needed to supply low, 24v, voltage and for ignition control.

- A thermostat with terminals ⓇR (common) and ⓌW (heat) is required for automatic control.

3. GO STEP-BY-STEP THROUGH THE ELECTRICAL SEQUENCE
- 115v line voltage must be supplied to the plenum switch ⊤, the thermal limit switch ⊤ and the oil burner primary control terminals ⒧L₁ and ⒩N.
- When the thermostat closes on a temperature fall, a circuit is established between ⓇR and ⓌW in the thermostat and between ⓉT and ⓉT in the primary control. The circuit is completed through the low voltage side of the primary control transformer ⌇⌇, the normally-closed flame relay contacts ⊣⊢, the safety switch heater ⋀⋀⋀, the normally-closed safety switch ⊣⊢, and the burner motor relay coil (RELAY COIL).
- When energized, the burner motor relay coil closes two sets of normally open contacts ⊣⊢. One set completes a low voltage circuit that parallels the flame relay contacts and the safety switch heater circuit. The other set of contacts completes a line voltage circuit, through the normally closed thermal limit switch ⊤, to the burner motor (PUMP MOTOR) and the ignition transformer ⌇⌇.
- The ignition transformer creates a 10,000v arc between two electrodes ⌐⌐ to ignite the oil being pumped by the burner motor.
- If the oil is ignited, a cad cell flame detector ⊙ will detect the flame and complete a low-voltage circuit through the flame relay coil (RELAY COIL). When energized, the flame relay coil will open the flame relay contacts ⊣⊢ and interrupt the circuit to the safety switch heater ⋀⋀⋀.

- If the oil fails to ignite, or ignition ceases, the flame relay contacts ╫ will stay closed and the safety switch heater ⌇⌇⌇ will remain in the circuit. After several seconds, the heater will warp open the safety switch ╫ and interrupt the circuit to the burner motor relay ⊙, thereby opening all of the control circuits.

- The oil burner primary control will not recycle until the safety switch heater has cooled and the safety switch has been closed by pressing a manual reset button.

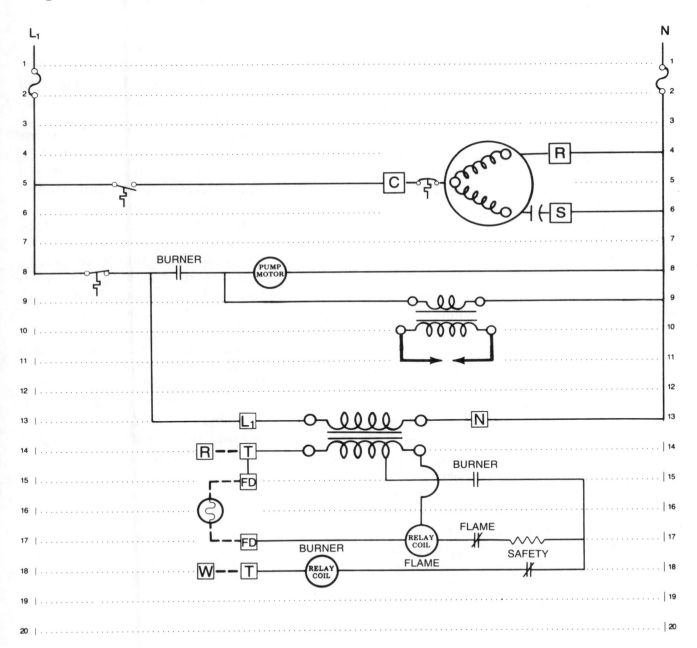

4. DRAW THE SCHEMATIC

STEP 1.   Insert fuses ⌇ in L_1 and N between lines 1 and 2.

STEP 2.   Draw an internal protector ⌇ for the indoor fan motor on line 5. Connect the run winding to N along line 4 and the start winding and start capacitor ⊣⊢ to N along line 6. Insert a normally-open plenum switch ⌇ on line 5 and connect it to L_1 and the internal protector.

STEP 3.   Draw a burner motor Ⓟ, on line 8. Draw a normally-closed thermal limit switch ⌇ and a set of normally-open burner motor relay contacts ⊣⊢, between L_1 and the burner motor. Connect the return side of the burner motor to N.

STEP 4.   Draw a step-up ignition transformer ⌇ on lines 9 and 10. Draw two electrodes ⌣ ⌣ on line 11 and connect them to the high side of the transformer. Connect one leg of the low side to N along line 9 and the other leg to line 8 at a point between the relay contacts and the burner motor.

STEP 5.   Draw a step-down transformer ⌇ on lines 13 and 14. Connect the 120v side to terminals L₁ and N of the burner primary control on line 13, and connect N to the line voltage neutral. Connect L₁ between the thermal limit switch ⌇ and burner motor contacts ⊣⊢ on line 8. This low voltage transformer and all of the low voltage circuits are integral parts of the burner primary control.

STEP 6.   Draw thermostat terminals R and W on lines 14 and 18. Draw the following terminals as part of the primary control: T on lines 14 and 18, FD on lines 15 and 17.

STEP 7.   Field wire ——— R to T on line 14, W to T on line 18. Connect T on line 14 to FD on line 15. Draw a flame detector ☺ on line 16 and field wire ——— it to FD and FD. Connect the 24v side of the transformer to T on line 14.

STEP 8.   On line 18, connect a burner motor relay coil (RELAY COIL) and a normally-closed safety switch ⊣⊬ to T. On line 17, connect a safety switch heater ⋀⋁⋀⋁, a normally-closed flame relay switch ⊣⊬, and the flame relay coil to FD.

STEP 9.   Draw a second set of burner motor contacts ⊣⊢ on line 15. Connect them to the transformer ⌇ tap and to the safety switch and the safety switch heater.

L_1 N

1	1
2	2
3	3
4	4
5	5
6	6
7	7
8	8
9	9
10	10
11	11
12	12
13	13
14	14
15	15
16	16
17	17
18	18
19	19
20	20

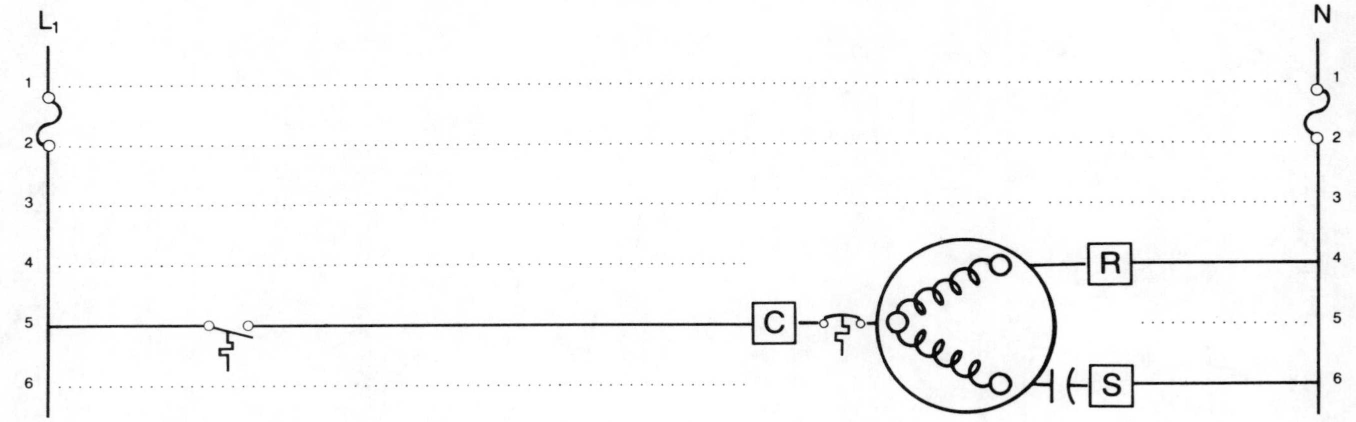

STEPS 1 AND 2

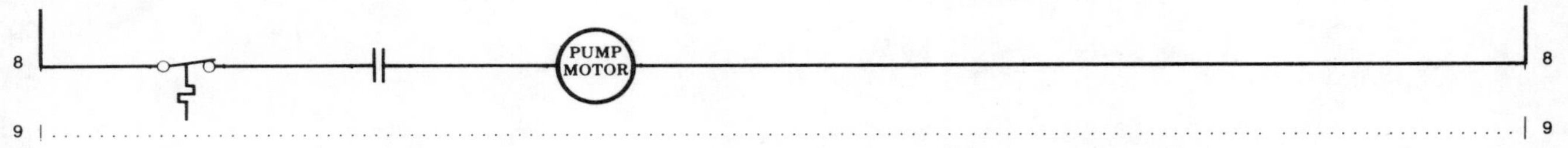

STEP 3

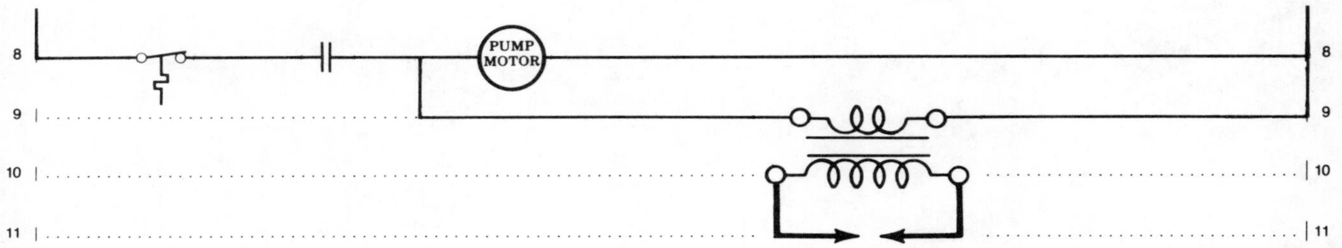

STEP 4

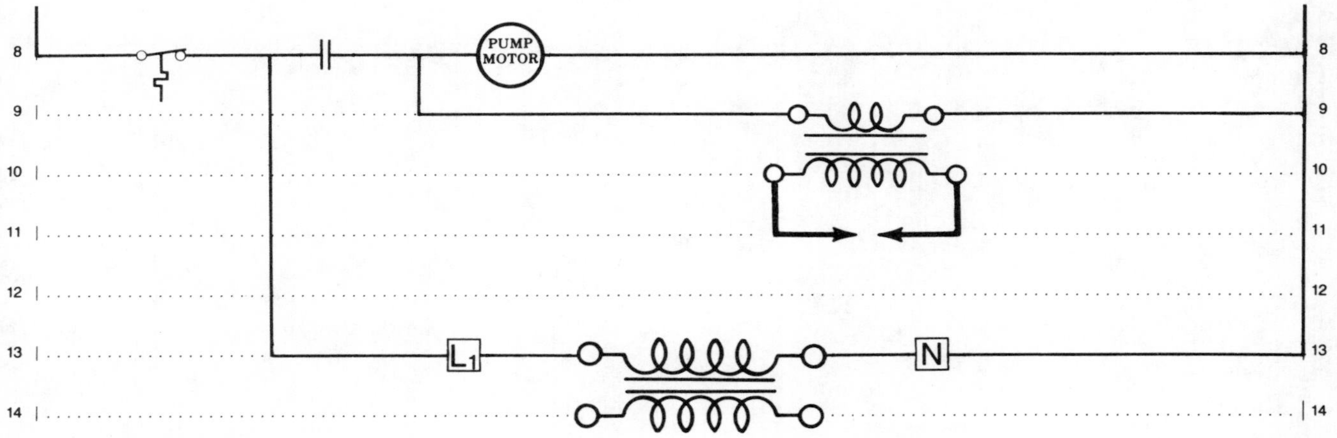

STEP 5

STEPS 6 AND 7

STEP 8

STEP 9

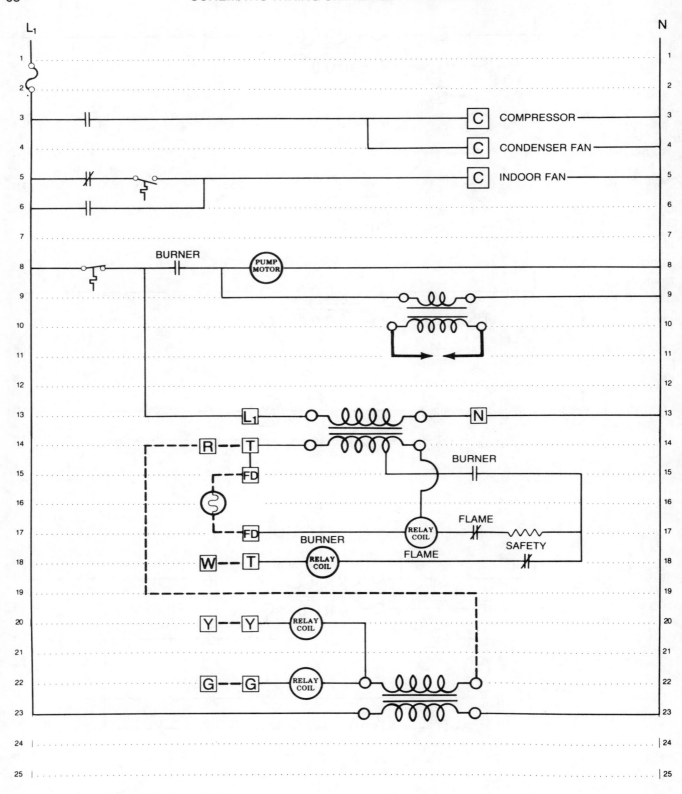

EXAMPLE 5
OIL-FIRED, FORCED AIR FURNACE WITH AUTOMATIC AIR CONDITIONING

This example shows how automatic air conditioning is added onto the oil-fired, forced air furnace shown in Example 4. Since the furnace schematic has been fully developed, this example will begin with the terminal center that links these two complementary systems.

1. DEFINE THE FUNCTION OF THE EQUIPMENT

This is an automatically-operated air conditioning system that works in conjunction with an existing oil-fired, forced air system.

2. LIST THE ELECTRICAL COMPONENTS
- A thermostat with terminals R (common), W (heat), Y (cooling) and G (fan) is required for automatic control.
- A fan relay with a coil (RELAY COIL) and one set of normally closed ⫫ and one set of normally open ⊣⊢ contacts is needed for fan operation during either heating or cooling.
- An internally-protected, permanent split capacitor compressor motor and condenser fan motor are both needed for cooling.
- A contactor relay with a coil (RELAY COIL) and a set of contacts ⊣⊢ is needed to start the compressor and condenser fan motors.
- A step-down transformer is needed to supply 24v power to the fan and cooling circuits.

3. GO STEP-BY-STEP THROUGH THE ELECTRICAL SEQUENCE
- When cooling is desired, the manual mode switch on the thermostat must be set on COOL. The manual fan control switch is usually on AUTO.
- When the thermostat closes on a temperature rise, a circuit is completed between terminals R and Y. This completes a circuit through the 24v side of the step-down transformer to the contactor coil (RELAY COIL). The contactor coil closes the contacts ⊣⊢ and completes parallel circuits to the start winding of the compressor and the condenser fan motors.
- At the same time, another circuit is completed from R to G, through the indoor fan relay coil (RELAY COIL). When the coil is energized, it opens the normally closed set of contacts ⫫ and closes the normally open set of contacts ⊣⊢. As a result, the normally open fan switch is bypassed and a circuit is completed to the start winding of the indoor fan motor.

4. DRAW THE SCHEMATIC

STEP 1. Redraw the burner primary control from Example 4, placing L̲₁̲ on line 13, T̲ on lines 14 and 18, F̲D̲ on lines 15 and 17. Fill in the remaining elements.

STEP 2. Draw the thermostat terminals: R̲ on line 14, W̲ on line 18, Y̲ on line 20, and G̲ on line 22.

STEP 3. Field wire ——— the burner primary control to the thermostat by connecting R̲ to T̲, W̲ to T̲.

On line 16, draw the flame detector ⊝ and field wire it to the F̲D̲ terminals.

STEP 4. Connect the line voltage side of a step-down transformer between L₁ and N on line 23. Connect the 24v side of the transformer to an indoor fan relay coil (RELAY COIL) on line 22 and connect the coil to terminal G̲. Draw a contactor coil (RELAY COIL) on line 20. Connect it to terminal Y̲ and to the 24v transformer on line 22. Connect the return side of the transformer to terminal R̲ on line 14. Connect Y̲ and G̲ to Y̲ and G̲ on the thermostat.

STEP 5. On line 5, draw a normally-closed set ⊣͟⊢ of indoor fan relay contacts and connect them to L₁ and a plenum switch ⌓. Connect the plenum switch to terminal C̲ of a PSC indoor fan motor. (Due to the lack of space, motors in this example will be indicated by a terminal C̲, even though the internal protector, the start and run windings, and the start capacitor have been previously shown.) On line 6, draw a normally-open set ⊣⊢ of indoor fan relay contacts and connect them to L₁ and to a point on line 5 between the plenum switch ⌓ and terminal C̲.

STEP 6. On line 3, draw a set of compressor contactors ⊣⊢ between L₁ and terminal C̲ of a PSC compressor motor.

STEP 7. On line 4, draw terminal C̲ of a PSC condenser fan motor and connect it to line 3 between the contactor and the compressor.

STEP 8. Starting on line 8, redraw the oil burner high side from Example 4. Indicate the junction of the burner primary transformer.

L₁   N

1 |..| 1

2 |..| 2

3 |..| 3

4 |..| 4

5 |..| 5

6 |..| 6

7 |..| 7

8 |..| 8

9 |..| 9

10 |..| 10

11 |..| 11

12 |..| 12

13 |..| 13

14 |..| 14

15 |..| 15

16 |..| 16

17 |..| 17

18 |..| 18

19 |..| 19

20 |..| 20

21 |..| 21

22 |..| 22

23 |..| 23

24 |..| 24

25 |..| 25

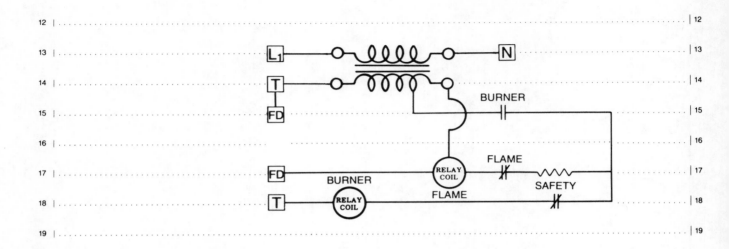

STEP 1

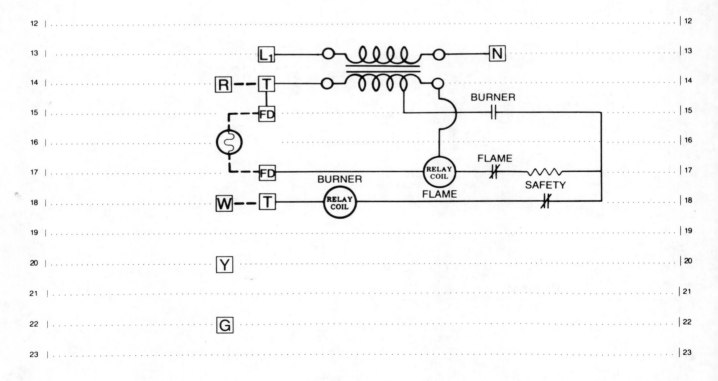

STEPS 2 AND 3

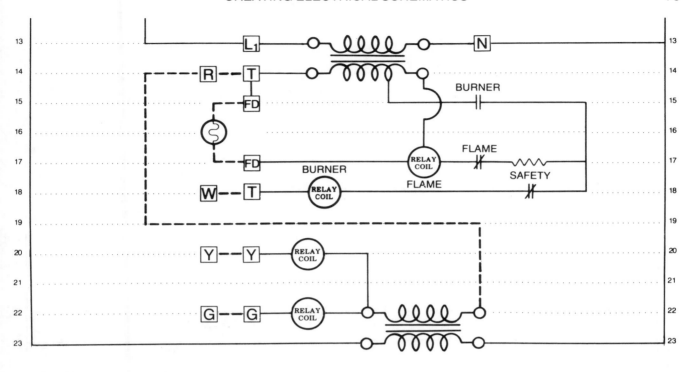

STEP 4

STEP 5

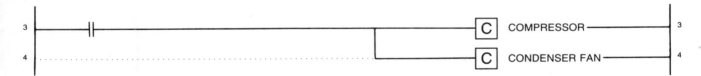

STEPS 6 AND 7

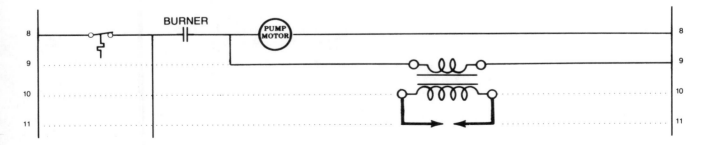

STEP 8

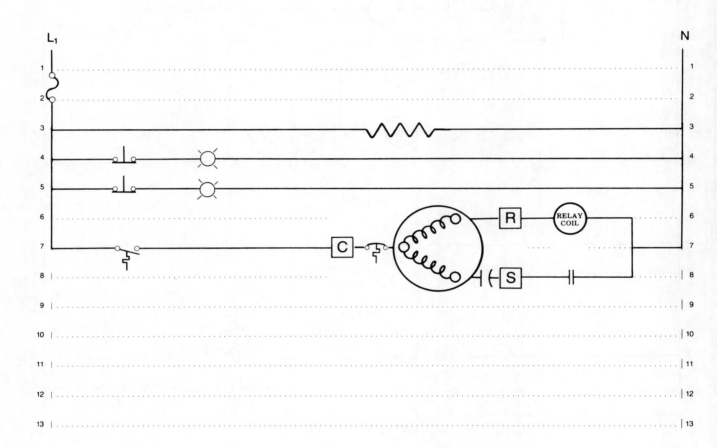

EXAMPLE 6
TWO-DOOR REFRIGERATOR/FREEZER

The domestic refrigerator/freezer is delivered as a complete unit and only needs to be plugged in to begin operating. This example will show only the basic electrical circuits used in low-cost units that do not feature automatic defrost.

1. DEFINE THE FUNCTION OF THE EQUIPMENT
   This is an automatically operated, refrigerator/freezer that that runs on line voltage and is equipped with a freezer door heater to prevent condensate from freezing the door shut.

2. LIST THE ELECTRICAL COMPONENTS
   * The standard electrical source is 115v, 60 cycle (60 Hz), single phase (1ϕ), alternating current (ac).
   * A fuse is ⌇ required by the Safety Code.
   * A freezer door heater ⟋⟍⟋⟍ is needed to prevent freezing of condensate at the door.
   * Light bulbs ⊘ are needed in both the refrigerator and freezer sections for greater visibility. They will be controlled by normally-closed push botton switches ₒ⊥ₒ that open when the door is closed.
   * A compressor is needed for cooling. It will have a high torque motor, equipped with a current (magnetic) relay.
   * A cooling thermostat ⌇ is needed for temperature control.

3. GO STEP-BY-STEP
   THROUGH THE ELECTRICAL SEQUENCE
   * Line voltage (115v, ac) must be supplied to all components.
   * There is no switch controlling the freezer door heater ⟋⟍⟋⟍, therefore is produces heat as long as power is available.
   * Lights ⊘ in the freezer and refrigerator compartments are controlled by normally-closed push button switches ₒ⊥ₒ that close when the door is open, completing a circuit to the light bulbs.
   * Cooling is provided by a refrigerant compressor whose internally protected motor is equipped with a current relay for extra starting torque. When the motor attains approximately 80% of full speed the starting relay drops out of the circuit.
   * The compressor is cycled on and off by a cooling thermostat ⌇ to maintain a pre-set temperature.

STEP 1

STEP 2

STEP 3

STEP 4

STEP 5

4. DRAW THE SCHEMATIC

STEP   1.   Draw in the line power (115v) using the two vertical lines L_1 and
N. Insert a fuse ⌇ in L_1 between
lines 1 and 2.

STEP   2.   On line 3, draw the freezer door
heater ⌁.

STEP   3.   On lines 4 and 5, draw a push button switch ₒ⌇ₒ and connect it to a
light bulb ⊗.

STEP   4.   On line 7, draw a cooling thermostat ⌁ and connect it to an internally-protected split phase motor
⌁. Draw a current relay, con-
sisting of a coil (RELAY COIL) on line 6 and a
pair of contacts ⊣⊢ on line 8, between the run and start windings
and connect it to N.

STEP   5.   Connect all of the elements thus
drawn to L_1 and N.

L_1 N

1 | | | 1
2 | | | 2
3 | | | 3
4 | | | 4
5 | | | 5
6 | | | 6
7 | | | 7
8 | | | 8
9 | | | 9
10 | | | 10
11 | | | 11
12 | | | 12
13 | | | 13

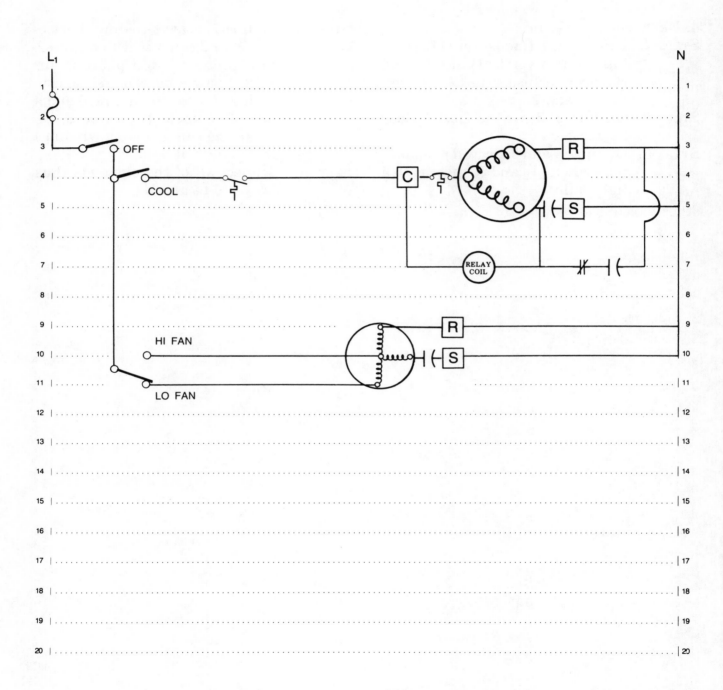

EXAMPLE 7
WINDOW AIR CONDITIONER

The typical window air conditioner is a plug-in unit that is completely wired by the manufacturer. While some window air conditioners have very involved electrical circuits, this example will cover only the basic, two-speed model.

One feature of note is the fan motor. This motor has a double-end shaft that drives two fans: one to circulate the indoor air, the other to cool the refrigerant condenser.

1. DEFINE THE FUNCTION OF THE EQUIPMENT

This is an automatically operated air conditioner with a two-speed motor that can be operated even when cooling is not required.

2. LIST THE ELECTRICAL COMPONENTS
- The standard home electrical source is 115v, 60 Hz, (1ϕ), ac current.
- A fuse ⌇ is required by the Safety Code.
- A selector switch is needed for mode control. This multi-position switch selects the following operating modes:

SWITCH POSITION	CONTACTS MADE
OFF	None
HI Fan	L_1 - HI
LO Fan	L_1 - LO
HI - Cool	L_1 - HI - Cool
LO - Cool	L_1 - LO - Cool

- A two-speed fan motor ⊕ is required for LO and HI Fan and Cool.
- A thermostat ⌀ is required for automatic control of the cooling compressor.
- A permanent split capacitor motor, with internal protector, is needed to drive the compressor.
- In areas that experience persistent low voltage, a hard-start kit may be required.

3. GO STEP-BY-STEP THROUGH THE ELECTRICAL SEQUENCE
- Line voltage (115v, ac) must be supplied to the unit.
- Cycling of the cooling compressor is controlled by a cooling thermostat when the manually-operated selector switch is on Cool.
- The compressor motor is an internally protected PSC type with an optional hard start kit composed of a start capacitor and a potential relay.
- The two-speed fan motor is essentially a PSC type with a run capacitor and an added low speed coil. It is controlled by a manually operated mode switch that allows it to operate independently of the cooling compressor.

4. DRAW THE SCHEMATIC

STEP   1.   Insert a fuse ⌇ in L_1 between line 1 and line 2.

STEP   2.   Draw single pole, single throw switches ⌒ on lines 3 and 4 and connect them in series.

STEP   3.   Connect the switch on line 4 to a cooling thermostat ⌇ and terminal ⒞ of a PSC motor ⊙. Connect terminals ⓡ and ⓢ to N.

STEP   4.   Draw the potential relay on line 7. Connect the relay coil (RELAY COIL) to terminal ⒞ and to a normally-closed switch ⌗ and a capacitor ⊣⊢. Connect the capacitor to the Run circuit and the relay coil to the Start circuit.

STEP   5.   Draw a two-speed motor ⊕ with the ⓡ terminal on line 9. Connect terminals ⓡ and ⓢ to N.

STEP   6.   Draw a single pole, double throw switch ⌒ with its terminals on lines 10 and 11. Connect its common terminal to the OFF switch on line 3. Connect the switch terminals to the two-speed motor and label the lines HI FAN and LO FAN.

L₁   N

```
   |                                                                      |
1  | . . . . . . . . . . . . . . . . . . . . . . . . . . . . . . . . . . | 1
2  | . . . . . . . . . . . . . . . . . . . . . . . . . . . . . . . . . . | 2
3  | . . . . . . . . . . . . . . . . . . . . . . . . . . . . . . . . . . | 3
4  | . . . . . . . . . . . . . . . . . . . . . . . . . . . . . . . . . . | 4
5  | . . . . . . . . . . . . . . . . . . . . . . . . . . . . . . . . . . | 5
6  | . . . . . . . . . . . . . . . . . . . . . . . . . . . . . . . . . . | 6
7  | . . . . . . . . . . . . . . . . . . . . . . . . . . . . . . . . . . | 7
8  | . . . . . . . . . . . . . . . . . . . . . . . . . . . . . . . . . . | 8
9  | . . . . . . . . . . . . . . . . . . . . . . . . . . . . . . . . . . | 9
10 | . . . . . . . . . . . . . . . . . . . . . . . . . . . . . . . . . . | 10
11 | . . . . . . . . . . . . . . . . . . . . . . . . . . . . . . . . . . | 11
12 | . . . . . . . . . . . . . . . . . . . . . . . . . . . . . . . . . . | 12
13 | . . . . . . . . . . . . . . . . . . . . . . . . . . . . . . . . . . | 13
14 | . . . . . . . . . . . . . . . . . . . . . . . . . . . . . . . . . . | 14
15 | . . . . . . . . . . . . . . . . . . . . . . . . . . . . . . . . . . | 15
16 | . . . . . . . . . . . . . . . . . . . . . . . . . . . . . . . . . . | 16
17 | . . . . . . . . . . . . . . . . . . . . . . . . . . . . . . . . . . | 17
18 | . . . . . . . . . . . . . . . . . . . . . . . . . . . . . . . . . . | 18
19 | . . . . . . . . . . . . . . . . . . . . . . . . . . . . . . . . . . | 19
20 | . . . . . . . . . . . . . . . . . . . . . . . . . . . . . . . . . . | 20
```

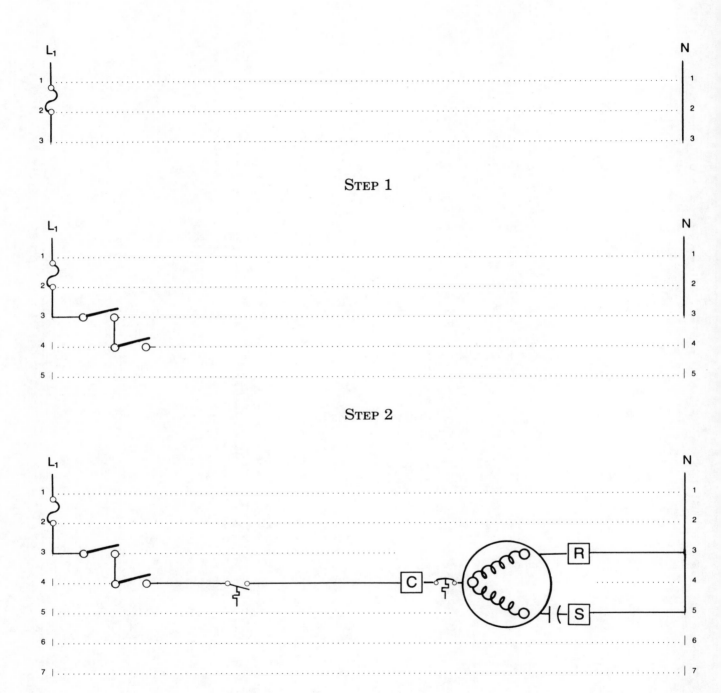

STEP 1

STEP 2

STEP 3

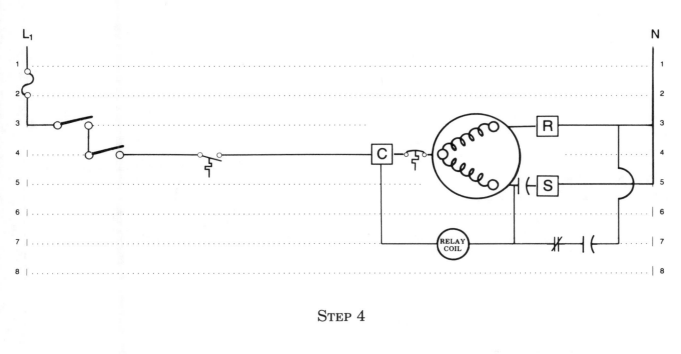

STEP 4

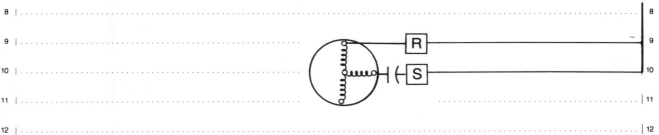

STEP 5

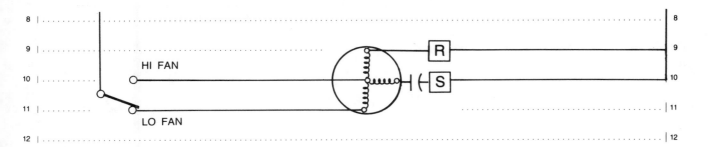

STEP 6

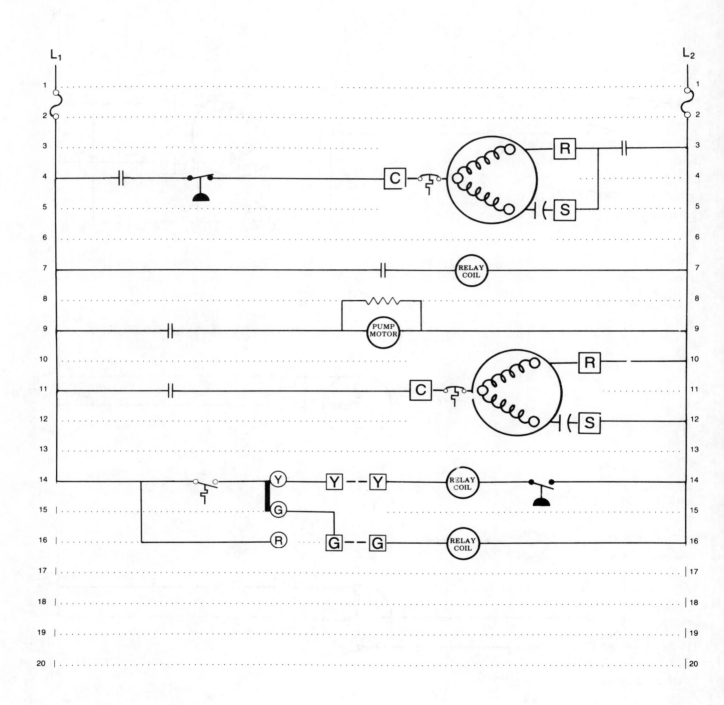

EXAMPLE 8
PACKAGE AIR CONDITIONER
WITH WATER COOLED CONDENSER

This package unit uses water as a condensing medium. The water pump is mounted in the equipment case and the only piping needed is a supply and return water line to the condenser. The selector switch and thermostat are located on the front of the package and all controls are line voltage.

1. DEFINE THE FUNCTION OF THE EQUIPMENT
This is an automatically operated air conditioning unit with a water-cooled condenser and line voltage controls.

2. LIST THE ELECTRICAL COMPONENTS
- The primary voltage is 220v, 60 Hz, 1φ, ac.
- Fuses ⌇ are required by the Safety Code.
- The compressor and indoor fan employ PSC motors ⊡-⦿-⊞. A water pump motor ⦿ is also required.
- Relays ⦿ are used to close the contacts for all three motors.
- A high pressure ⊥ and low pressure ⊥ control are used to protect the compressor.
- Because the water pump must start before the compressor, a time delay relay ⋀⋀⋀, with a 60 second delay, will be used.
- The selector switch has three positions: OFF, nothing operates; FAN, only the fan runs; COOL, both the compressor and the fan run.
- The compressor is cycled by a line voltage cooling thermostat ⊥.

3. GO STEP-BY-STEP THROUGH THE ELECTRICAL SEQUENCE
- Line voltage (220v) must be supplied to the unit.
- With the selector switch on FAN, the fan relay ⦿ is energized, closing the contacts ⊣⊢ to the fan motor ⊡-⦿-⊞.
- With the selector switch on COOL the fan will run. When the thermostat closes, on a call for cooling, the water pump relay coil will be energized, closing the water pump contacts on line 9, if the low pressure control ⊥ is closed.
- With the water pump running, the time delay relay heater ⋀⋀⋀ is energized. After 60 seconds it will close the contacts on line 7 and energize the compressor contacter coil, if the high pressure switch ⊥ is closed. Thus, the compressor cannot start until after the the condenser cooling water is circulating.

4. DRAW THE SCHEMATIC

STEP 1. Insert fuses ⌇ in L₁ and L₂ between lines 1 and 2.

STEP 2. Draw an internally protected PSC compressor motor ⊙ with terminal Ⓒ on line 4. Link terminal Ⓒ to a high pressure switch ⊥, a set of contacts ⊣⊢, and L₁. On line 3, insert a pair of contacts and join terminal Ⓢ to Ⓡ to L₂.

STEP 3. Insert a set of contacts and wire the water pump ⊙ between L₁ and L₂ on line 9.

STEP 4. On line 11, draw a set of contacts and wire them between L₁ and terminal Ⓒ of a PSC indoor fan motor. Join terminals Ⓢ and Ⓡ of the motor to L₂.

STEP 5. Draw a thermostat switch ⊥ on line 14. Show the thermostat connections by field wiring a pair of terminals Ⓨ on line 14 and Ⓖ on line 16. Draw the internal thermostat contacts: Ⓨ on line 14, Ⓖ on line 15, and Ⓡ on line 16. Connect Ⓨ and Ⓖ with a manual slide switch ⏐. Connect Ⓖ to Ⓖ and Ⓡ to L₁ at line 14.

STEP 6. On line 14, connect the water pump relay and a low pressure switch ⊥ to Ⓨ and L₂.

STEP 7. On line 16, connect the indoor fan relay coil ⊙ to Ⓖ and L₂.

STEP 8. On line 7, insert the time delay relay contacts ⊣⊢ and the compressor contactor coil ⊙, in series, between L₁ and L₂.

On line 9, draw the pump motor ⊙ and its contacts ⊣⊢.

STEP 9. Add the time delay relay heater ⌁ on line 8, in a parallel circuit to the water pump and in series with the water pump contactor contacts ⊣⊢ on line 9.

L₁   N

1			1
2			2
3			3
4			4
5			5
6			6
7			7
8			8
9			9
10			10
11			11
12			12
13			13
14			14
15			15
16			16
17			17
18			18
19			19
20			20

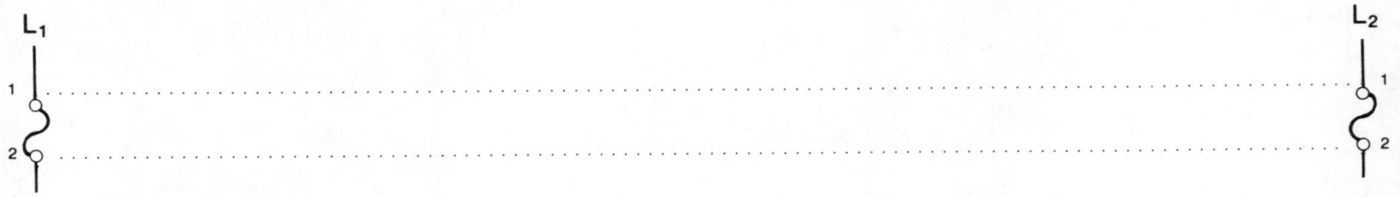

L₁   L₂

STEP 1

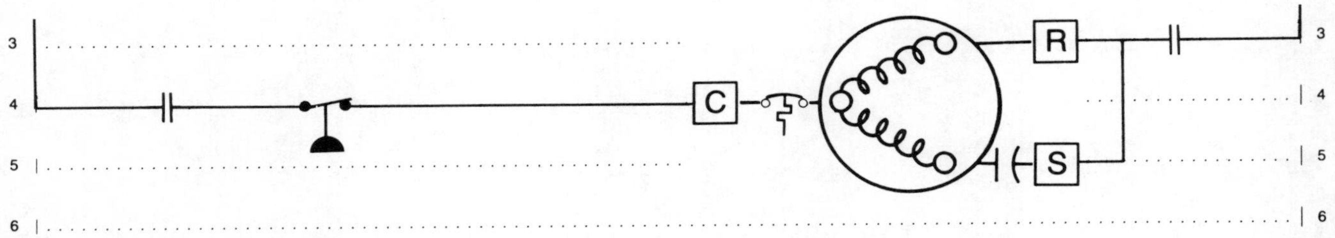

STEP 2

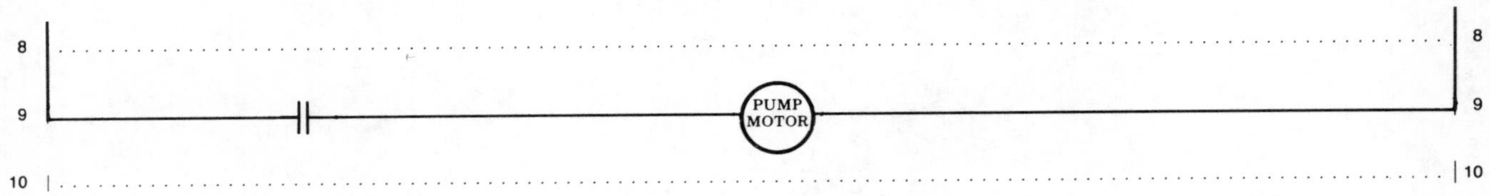

STEP 3

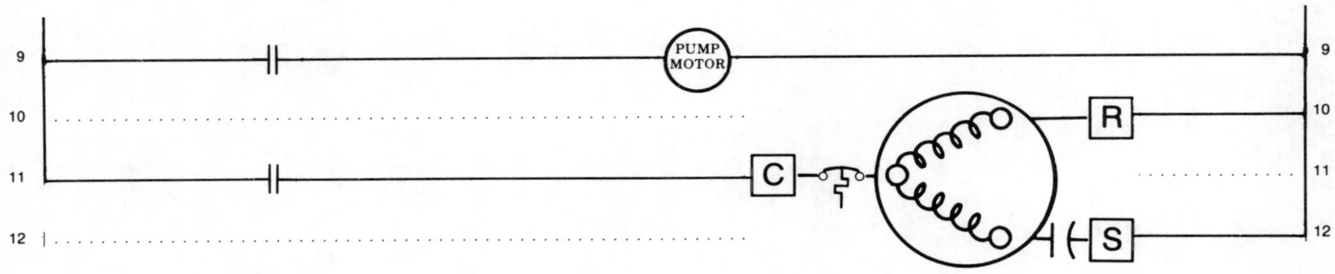

STEP 4

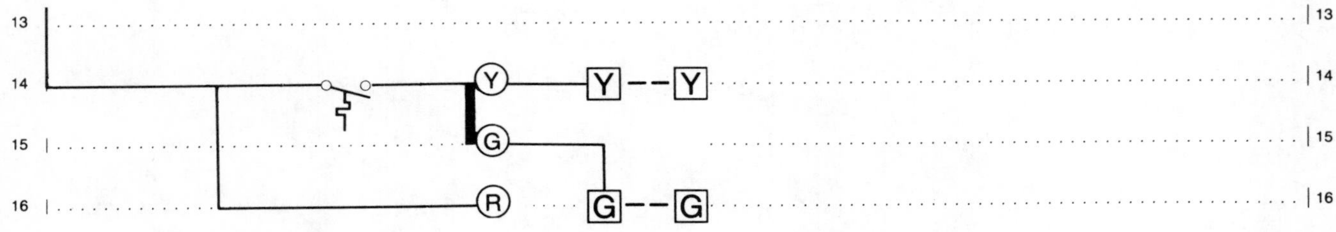

STEP 5

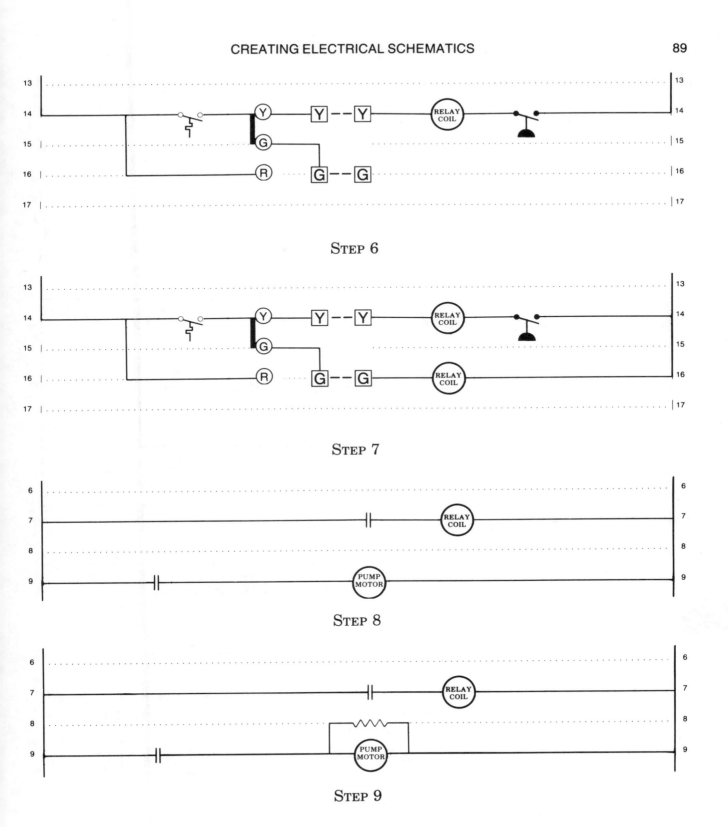

STEP 6

STEP 7

STEP 8

STEP 9

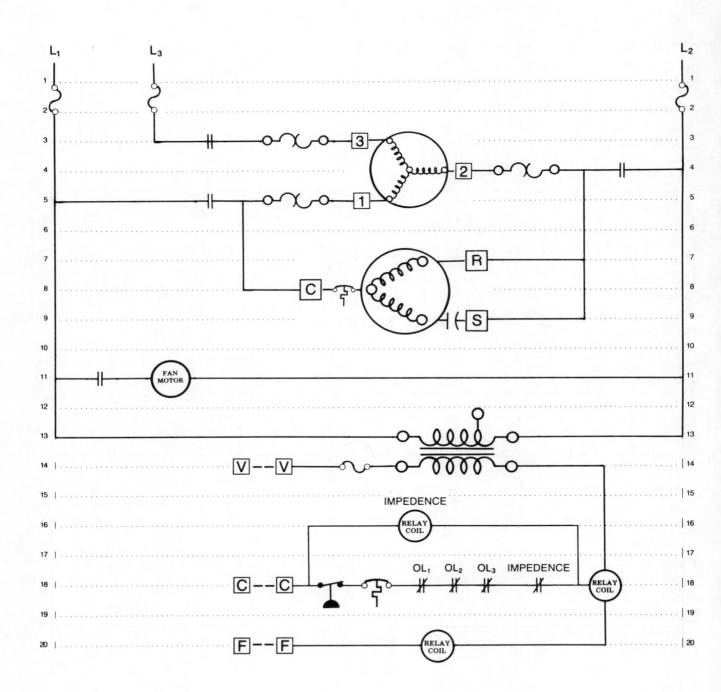

EXAMPLE 9
SINGLE PACKAGE
AIR COOLED AIR CONDITIONER

This package unit is a complete factory-wired system, except for the low voltage (24v) remote thermostat. The primary voltage to the unit will be 220v/208v, 3φ, 60 Hz.

1. DEFINE THE FUNCTION OF THE EQUIPMENT
  This is an automatically controlled air conditioner with a 3φ compressor.

2. LIST THE ELECTRICAL EQUIPMENT
* The electrical source is 220/208v, 60 Hz, 3φ, ac current.
* Fuses ⌇ are required by the Safety Code.
* A 3φ motor ⬩ with thermal ⌁ protectors is required for cooling.
* A contactor, consisting of a relay coil ⬩ and contacts ⚟ in each of the three-phase lines, is needed to start the compressor.
* Each of the three-phase leads should be protected by an overload ⚟ in the 24v cooling circuit.
* Additional protection is provided by a high pressure switch ⊥ and a compressor motor thermal protector ⬩ in the 24v circuit.
* An impedence relay is to be used to prevent automatic restarting after a safety device has opened.
* A single phase, PSC motor ⬩ is needed to cool the condenser. It is operated in tandem with the compressor.
* An indoor fan motor ⬩ is needed to circulate the cooled air. A fan relay ⬩ controls this motor.
* A 220v step-down transformer, with a 208v tap ⬩, is needed to supply 24v current to the low voltage circuit. The low side of the transformer is protected by a fuse ⌁.
* A thermostat, with terminals V, C, and F is needed for automatic control.

3. GO STEP-BY STEP
  THROUGH THE ELECTRICAL SEQUENCE
* Set the thermostat on COOL, fan on AUTO, and lower the temperature setting to close contacts V to C and F.
* With all of the safety control contacts ⊥, ⬩, ⚟ closed, the contactor coil ⬩ and the indoor fan relay coil ⬩ will be energized. Three sets of contacts ⊣⊢ will close, starting the compressor ⬩ and the outdoor fan motor ⬩.
* The indoor fan motor ⬩ will also start when its contacts close.
* If any safety control opens, only the compressor and the outdoor fan motor will stop.
* The opening of the thermostat contacts V to F will stop the indoor fan motor.
* If any safety device opens, the cause of the interruption must be determined and corrected, and the impedence relay manually reset, before normal operation can resume.

4. DRAW THE SCHEMATIC

STEP   1. Start with the high voltage (220v) section. Draw in lines L_1, L_2, L_3 above line 1. Fuse ⌇ each of the power lines between lines 1 and 2.

STEP   2. Draw the three phase compressor ⏦, with lead ② on line 4, the outdoor fan PSC motor ⏦, with lead Ⓒ on line 8.

STEP   3. Add the external overloads ⌁, in L_1, L_2, and L_3 after the ⌇.

STEP   4. Place contacts ‖ between the fuse and the overload on lines 3, 4 and 5.

STEP   5. The wiring in STEP 4 shows control for the compressor only. Wire the outdoor fan motor to start and stop with the compressor by connecting it from L_1 to L_2 on the load side of the contacts ‖ and outside the overloads ⌁.

STEP   6. On line 11, draw the indoor fan motor and its contacts. Draw the 220v step-down transformer ⌇ with a 208v tap, on lines 13 and 14. Connect all of these elements to L_1 and L_2.

This completes the high voltage section. Re-check your drawing and then start the low voltage control circuit.

STEP   7. Protect the low side of the transformer with a ⌁ on line 14.

STEP   8. Draw a pair of field wired terminals Ⓥ on line 14, Ⓒ on line 18, Ⓕ on line 20.

STEP   9. On line 18, draw the compressor contactor coil (RELAY COIL) and connect it to the transformer.

STEP 10. While on line 18, add the safety controls to protect the compressor. First put in the high pressure switch ⏌, followed by the internal protector ⌇. This switch is in the compressor, but opens in the low voltage circuit. Now add the three overload contacts $\overset{OL_1}{\#}$ and connect all these safety devices to terminal Ⓒ.

STEP 11. On line 16, draw in the high impedance relay coil (RELAY COIL), in series with the contactor coil (RELAY COIL), (as described in Section II). The normally closed contacts ╫ of the impedance relay are on line 18 and in series with the contactor coil.

STEP 12. On line 20 install the indoor fan relay coil (RELAY COIL), and complete the wiring from terminal Ⓕ.

You have now completed the schematic for the package unit. Go over the steps again until you have a complete understanding of how the low voltage circuit controls the operation of the system from the thermostat.

L₁

1
2
3
4
5
6
7
8
9
10
11
12
13
14
15
16
17
18
19
20

Step 1

Step 2

Step 3

STEP 4

STEP 6

STEP 7

STEP 8

STEP 9

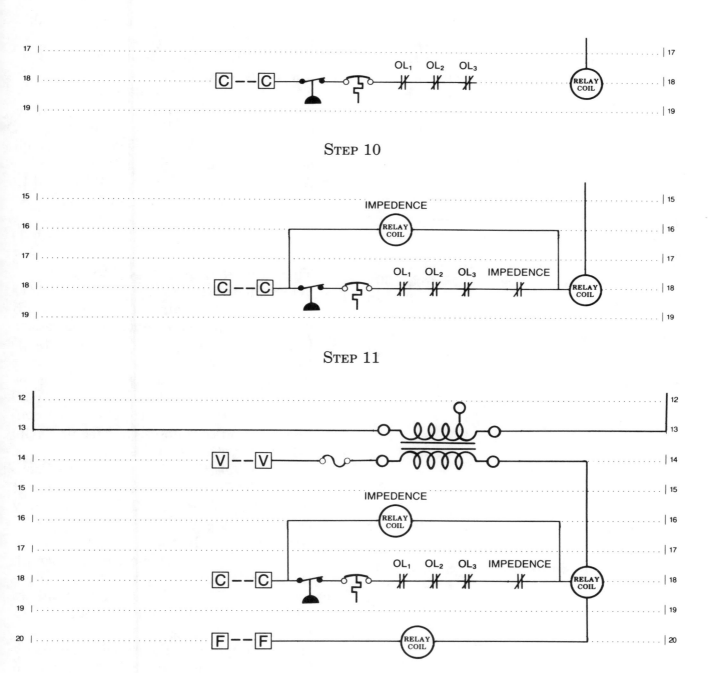

STEP 10

STEP 11

STEP 12

EXAMPLE 10
ELECTRIC HOT AIR FURNACE

During the past few years, electric resistance hot air furnaces have been gaining in popularity, especially in areas where natural gas is either scarce or expensive.

One of the problems with electric heat is the surge in power demand which is expensive for utilities. Therefore, as you will see, electric furnaces are designed to bring the power on in steps rather than in one massive surge.

The unit that we will now examine is supplied as a complete, factory-wired package, lacking only the thermostat.

1. DEFINE THE FUNCTION OF THE EQUIPMENT

This is an automatically-operated, 230v, electric resistance, hot air furnace, designed to energize the heating elements in three steps. Due to the high amperage, all high voltage circuits are doubly fused and all heating elements are isolated by additional fuses. For added safety, each heating stage is equipped with a thermal limit switch that opens if the fan fails or any malfunction leads to overheating.

LIST THE ELECTRIC COMPONENTS

- A 230v, 60 Hz, single phase (1ϕ), ac power source is required.
- A fuse ⌇ is required by the Safety Code.
- A thermostat ⊤, with terminals V (common), H (heat), and F (fan) is needed for automatic control.
- A permanent split capacitor motor ⊙ⓜ is required for hot air distribution.
- A fan relay coil (RELAY COIL) and fan relay contacts ⊣⊢ are needed for fan control.
- Three pairs of resistance heating elements ∘�misᴴᵀᴿmisᴇ∘, each separated by a fusible link ∿, are required for heat output.

- Each high voltage circuit must be doubly protected by cartridge fuses ⊏⊐.
- Each heating stage is protected by a thermal limit switch ⊤̣.
- Each stage is sequenced by a time delay relay composed of a heater ⌇ᵀᴿ and and two sets of normally-open contacts ⊣ᵀᴿ⁻²⊢, one set in the low voltage circuit, the other in the high voltage circuit.
- A step down transformer will be used to supply 24v power to the control circuits.

3. GO STEP-BY-STEP
THROUGH THE ELECTRICAL SEQUENCE

- When the thermostat ⊤ closes, on a temperature drop, it completes a circuit from V to H and F. This energizes the indoor fan relay coil and closes the contacts ⊣⊢ to the fan motor ⊙ⓜ.
- A second circuit, through H, energizes the 1TR time delay heater ⌇ᵀᴿ. After 20 seconds, the heater closes the 1TR-1 contacts ⊣ᵀᴿ⁻¹⊢ and completes the circuit to the 1HTR first stage heaters ∘�misᴴᵀᴿmisᇰ∘.
- At the same time, a second set of contacts, 1TR-2, close and complete a circuit to the second stage, 2TR, time delay relay heater.
- After 20 seconds, the second time delay heater, 2TR, completes a circuit through the 2TR-1 contacts to the second stage heaters 2HTR and, through contacts 2TR-2, to the third stage time delay heater, 3TR.
- After 20 seconds, the third time delay heater, 3TR, closes the 3TR-1 contacts to the third stage heater, 3HTR.

• Should localized heating occur at any one of the heaters, the closest thermal limit switch ⌐⌐ will open and interrupt the circuit at that stage. If the overheating is widespread, due to fan failure, all three thermal limit switches will open and cut off the heaters, even while the thermostat continues to call for heat.

• If there is a short, or any other source of excess amperage, the fusible links ∿ will melt open and isolate the overloaded circuit or component.

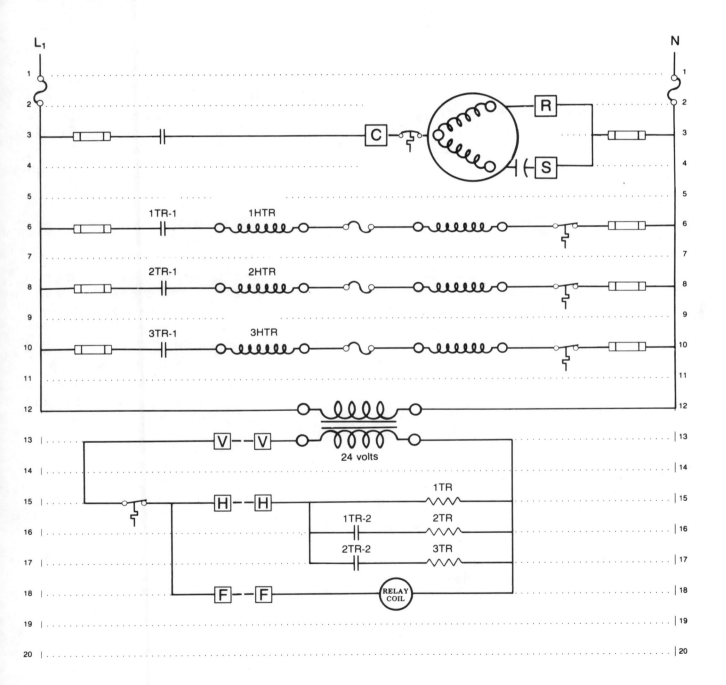

4. Draw the Schematic

STEP 1. Insert a fuse ⌇ in L_1 and L_2 between lines 1 and 2.

STEP 2. On line 3, draw a cartridge fuse ⊏⊐, the contacts ┤├ of the indoor fan relay, and a PSC motor. Join the run R and start S windings and connect them to a cartridge fuse which is joined to line L_2 on line 3.

STEP 3. On line 6, draw a cartridge fuse ⊏⊐, the contacts for the 1TR-1 time delay relay, a heater coil, a fusible link ∿, another heater coil, a thermal limit switch, and another cartridge fuse. Connect this array in series with L_1 and L_2.

STEP 4. Repeat STEP 3 on line 8 and again on line 10, changing the labels on the relay contacts and heater coils to indicate that they are in, respectively, the second and third heating stages.

STEP 5. Draw the 230v side of a step-down transformer on line 12, the 24v side on line 13. Connect the 24v side to terminal V on line 13.

STEP 6. On line 18, draw terminal F and the indoor fan relay coil.

STEP 7. On line 15, draw terminal H and the 1TR heater for the first time delay relay.

STEP 8. On line 16, draw the 1TR-2 contacts for the first time delay relay and the 2TR heater for the second time delay relay.

STEP 9. On line 17, draw the 2TR-2 contacts for the second time delay relay and the 3TR heater for the third time delay relay.

STEP 10. Connect the TR heaters and contacts on lines 15, 16, and 17 to terminal H. Connect all of the low voltage circuits to the return side of the transformer on line 13.

STEP 11. Draw the thermostat. On line 15, draw a normally-closed thermal switch and connect it to terminal H. Connect the thermal switch to terminal V on line 13. Draw terminal F on line 16 and connect it to line 15 between the thermal switch and H. To complete the schematic, field wire ——— the matching terminals to the thermostat.

L₁   N

1 |. . . . . | 1

2 |. . . . . | 2

3 |. . . . . | 3

4 |. . . . . | 4

5 |. . . . . | 5

6 |. . . . . | 6

7 |. . . . . | 7

8 |. . . . . | 8

9 |. . . . . | 9

10 |. . . . . | 10

11 |. . . . . | 11

12 |. . . . . | 12

13 |. . . . . | 13

14 |. . . . . | 14

15 |. . . . . | 15

16 |. . . . . | 16

17 |. . . . . | 17

18 |. . . . . | 18

19 |. . . . . | 19

20 |. . . . . | 20

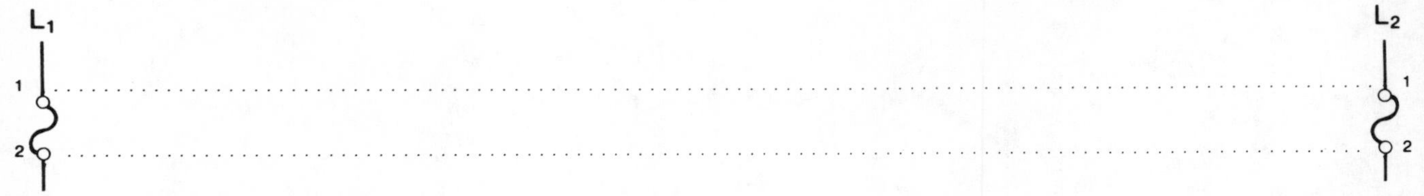

STEP 1

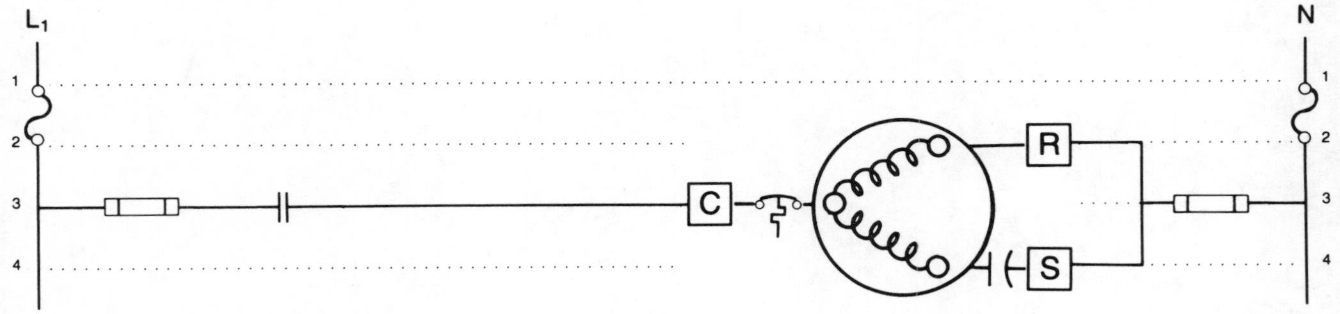

STEP 2

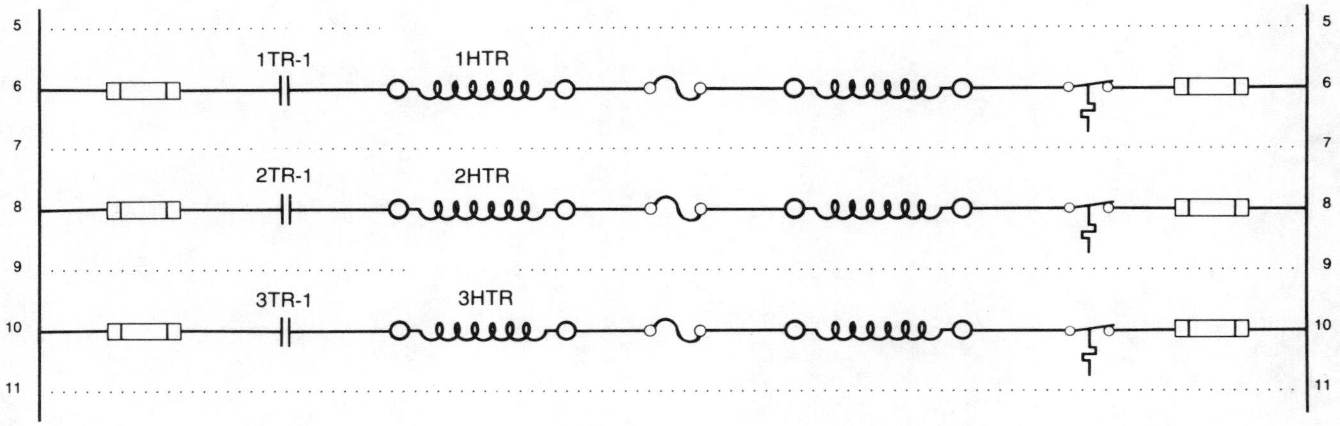

STEPS 3 AND 4

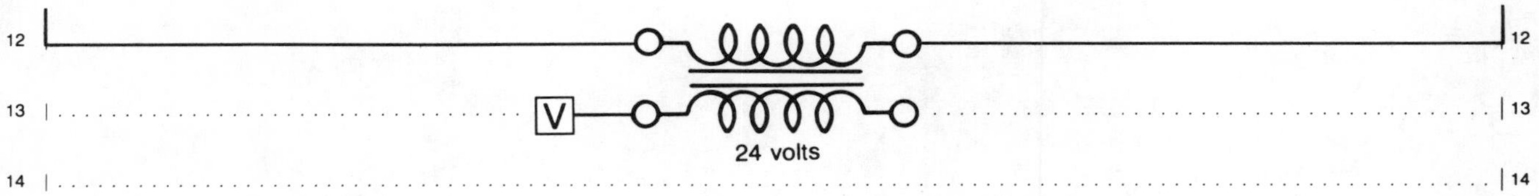

24 volts

STEP 5

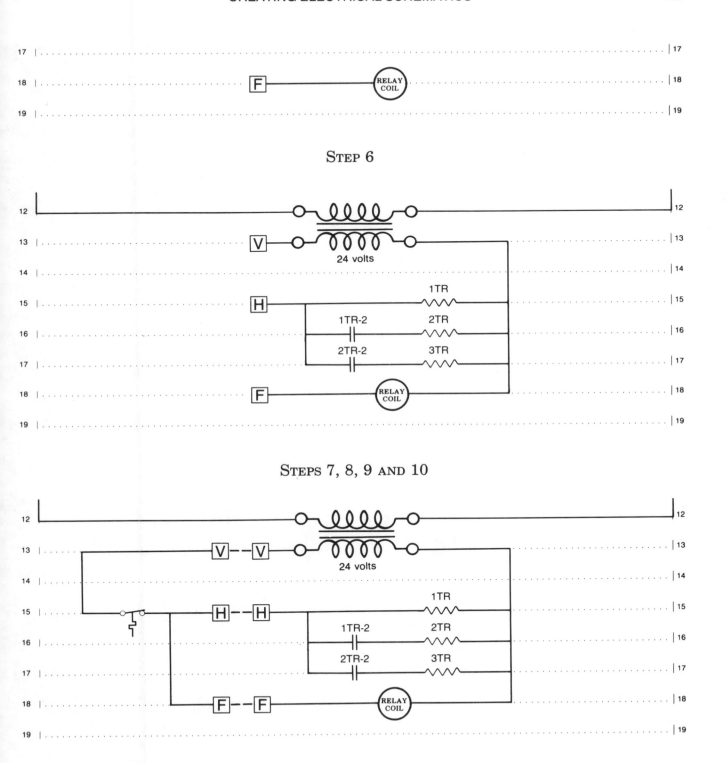

STEP 6

STEPS 7, 8, 9 AND 10

STEP 11

Section V

MANUFACTURERS' SCHEMATICS

THE WIRING DIAGRAM

A wiring or connection diagram, sometimes called a pictorial, will accompany most schematic drawings. Unlike the schematic, the wiring diagram will indicate the general position of each electrical device such as relays, disconnects, motors, transformers, switch contacts, capacitors, etc. Some wiring diagrams will indicate the color of each wire and some will show the identifying numbers appearing on the wires.

Figure 5-1 is a typical wiring diagram. It indicates the boundary of the control panel, with all the devices within the panel shown in their relative positions. External items are shown outside the panel boundary with some indication of their location relative to the panel. In some cases, related items cannot be easily shown on the diagram. When this happens, the manufacturer will usually note, on the diagram, where the unshown device is located.

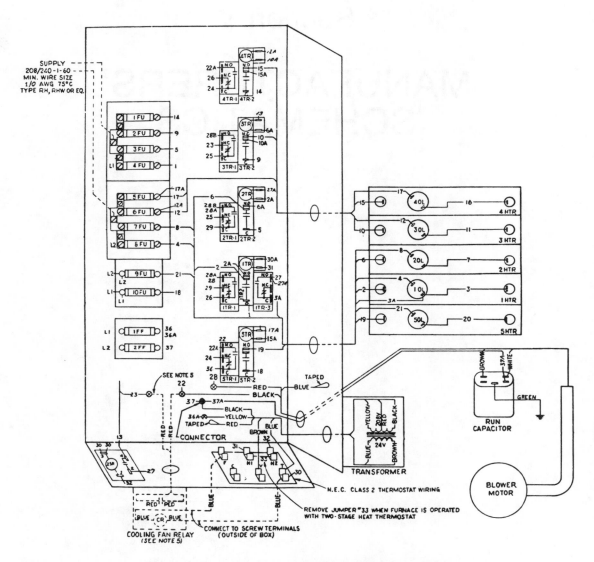

FIG. 5-1. *Courtesy York Division, Borg-Warner Corp.*

Wiring, on the connection diagram, is shown in a number of ways. The three most popular methods are:

1. Each wire is drawn from terminal to terminal. A good illustration of this method is the wiring diagram for the Frigidaire side-by-side refrigerator/freezer, including the optional ice maker and butter conditioner, Figure 5-2. This wiring diagram shows every wire and electrical device in a pictorial fashion.

2. Groups of wires are shown as a harness, with single wires connected at each component. York uses this method very effectively, Figure 5-3, in routing the four wires from the FAN MOTOR. York also prints identifying numbers on each wire to make circuit tracing much easier.

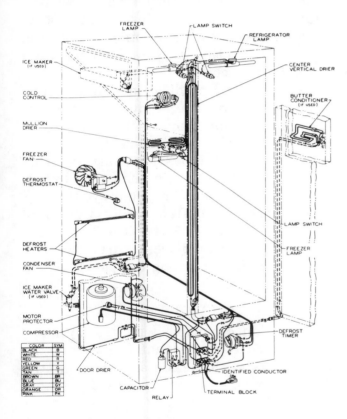

FIG. 5-2. *Courtesy Frigidaire Div.*

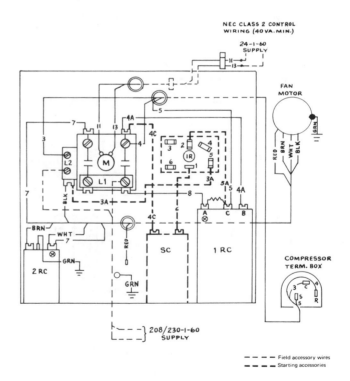

FIG. 5-3. *Courtesy York Division, Borg-Warner Corp.*

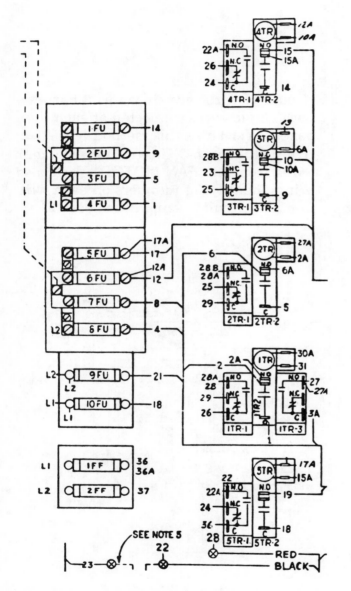

FIG. 5-4. *Courtesy York Division, Borg-Warner Corp.*

3. Show little or no wiring from terminal to terminal. Figure 5-4 is typical of this method which is being adopted by more manufacturers. Note that each terminal is assigned a number. You can conclude that each pair of terminals having matching numbers is joined by wiring. Identical numbers are used on the schematic, making it easy to move from the schematic to the pictorial drawing when tracing a circuit.

This method produces a cleaner drawing that is uncluttered by a maze of wiring. But it may prove difficult for beginners who are accustomed to tracing a line from point to point. Once mastered, this style will prove to be much easier to use. With no wires to follow, your eyes are not distracted. Very often, where a group of wires is drawn close together, your eye will skip to an adjacent wire that misleads you to the wrong component.

Connection diagrams will usually show the coil and contacts that are within the components, with the contacts shown in the normally open or normally closed position.

Remember, the pictorial or connection or wiring diagram is used to locate the defective component . . . after the potential problem has been isolated on the schematic diagram.

TROUBLESHOOTING THE ELECTRICAL CIRCUIT

The electrical schematics shown in the following examples are for heating, cooling and refrigeration units that are in use today. They were selected to demonstrate the many different styles used by manufacturers in their schematics.

Before you proceed, you must have a system or plan for using the schematic to isolate the electrical breakdown in the circuit. Without a system, it is easy to overlook or forget a less obvious point and misdiagnose the problem.

Here is a recommended plan of procedure that has proved very effective over the years. There are five steps:

STEP 1. Read the schematic to determine the electrical sequence or *what happens next*. This is the most important step since it is almost impossible to troubleshoot any equipment without a prior knowledge of how it is supposed to operate. It is like troubleshooting a moon rocket without knowing the location of the start button.

STEP 2. Check the primary voltage to the equipment. It is not enough to say that there is voltage to the equipment, the question is how much voltage?

Many problems are no fault of the equipment, rather are due to an undetected voltage drop. Low voltage may be caused by undersize wire or overloaded transmission lines during summer's peak air conditioning hours.

Do not use a light tester or a neon tester to check voltage. They can only tell you that voltage is present. A voltmeter is needed to tell you exactly how much voltage is available.

STEP 3. Check fuses. It is safer, and will reduce mistakes, if the fuses are removed and checked with an ohmmeter or continuity tester.

STEP 4. Locate the device that does not function, whether it be a motor, solenoid, relay, etc.

STEP 5. Starting at the non-operating device, with the power on, use a voltmeter to check power flow through all contacts leading to the non-operative device.

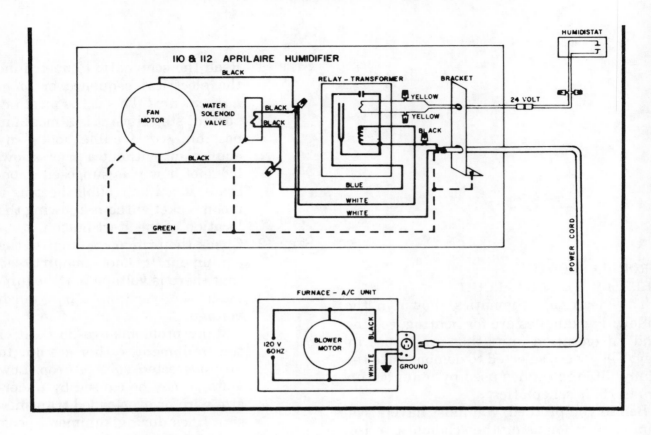

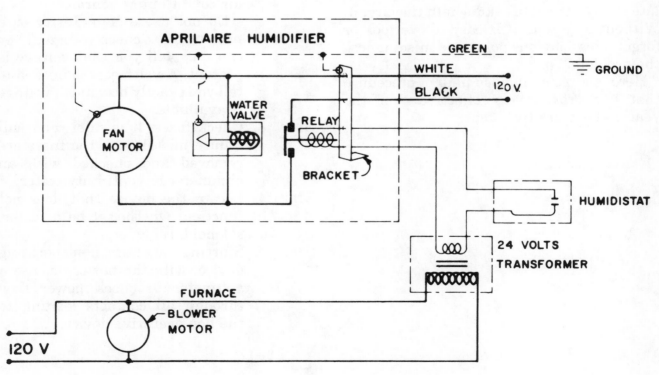

APRILAIRE MODEL 110 POWER HUMIDIFIER

During the heating season, warmed indoor air is continuously lost, through cracks around windows and doors, and replaced by cold outdoor air. When this cold outdoor air is heated, it expands, lowering the relative humidity and causing the air to be dry. The humidifier is used to restore needed moisture to the air to maintain a comfortable humidity level.

All humidifiers are dependent upon heat for evaporation. Humidifiers normally extract this heat from the hot air in the supply plenum at the top of the furnace.

The Aprilaire schematic is a good example of a small humidifier with a 24v control circuit —— and a 115v power circuit ——.

The control circuit draws electricity from the furnace blower motor 115v circuit to assure that the humidifier will only operate when the furnace blower is on. 115v, from the furnace blower circuit, is applied to the primary of the step-down transformer 🔲 which reduces the voltage to 24v.

The humidistat ▭ and coil of the electromagnetic relay ▭ are in the 24v circuit. The power circuit draws electricity from any standard 115v, 60 Hz supply.

Now, following the five-step troubleshooting procedure:

1. GO STEP-BY-STEP
THROUGH THE ELECTRICAL SEQUENCE

- Set the fan control switch on the thermostat to *auto*. This will complete the circuit to the blower motor ⟲ and simultaneously supply 115v to the transformer primary 🔲.
- Raise the setting on the humidistat to close the humidistat contacts ▭.
- With the humidistat contacts closed, a 24v circuit is completed from the low voltage side of the transformer to the relay coil ▭.
- The energized magnetic relay coil will close the relay contacts, completing two parallel 115v circuits. One 115v circuit will energize the solenoid coil ▭ of the water valve, opening the valve to feed water to the humidifier. The other 115v circuit will start the fan motor ⊕ to circulate warm furnace air through the humidifier.

By examining the schematic, it can now be seen that...

- The humidifier is totally inoperative when the furnace blower ⟲ is off.
- If the fan motor ⊕ fails, the water valve can still operate.
- If the water valve solenoid ▭ fails, the fan motor can still operate.
- A failure of the electromagnetic relay coil ▭, humidistat ▭, or transformer 🔲 will make the humidifier inoperative.

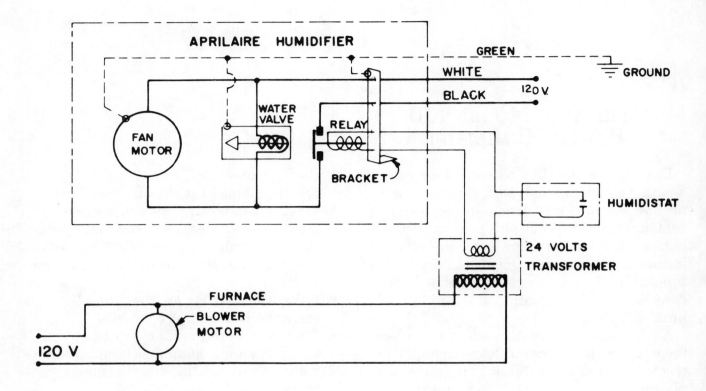

With the humidifier in operation, what voltmeter readings would you expect across the following:

1. Furnace blower motor
2. Humidifier fan motor
3. Water valve solenoid coil
4. Electromagnetic relay coil
5. Secondary of transformer
6. Humidistat contacts
7. Relay contacts

Using the five-step procedure outlined under *Troubleshooting the Electrical Circuit,* solve these two problems:

Problem 1. Fan motor will not operate. Furnace blower motor and water valve are operating.

STEP 1. The schematic has been read.

STEPS 2 and 3. The furnace blower motor and the water valve both operate, indicating that the fuses are good and that there is power to the humidifier.

STEP 4. The fan motor is not functioning.

STEP 5. Isolate and solve the problem using the voltmeter.

- The schematic shows that the only reasons the fan motor would not run are: either a defective fan motor or an open circuit to the fan motor.
- If the voltmeter shows 115v across the fan motor terminals, the motor is defective.
- If the voltmeter reads zero voltage across the fan motor terminals, there is an open circuit between the motor terminals and either L1 or neutral.
- If the voltmeter indicates 115v from one terminal of the fan motor to the neutral at the water valve connection, this line is open.
- If no voltage is indicated, read from the other terminal of the fan motor to the other connection of the water valve solenoid. You should read 115v, indicating that this line is open.
- Remember, the water valve solenoid is operative. This means that we have voltage to this point in the circuit.

Problem 2. The water valve and fan motor will not operate. The furnace blower motor is running and the humidistat contacts are closed. Find all of the possible causes that could create this condition.

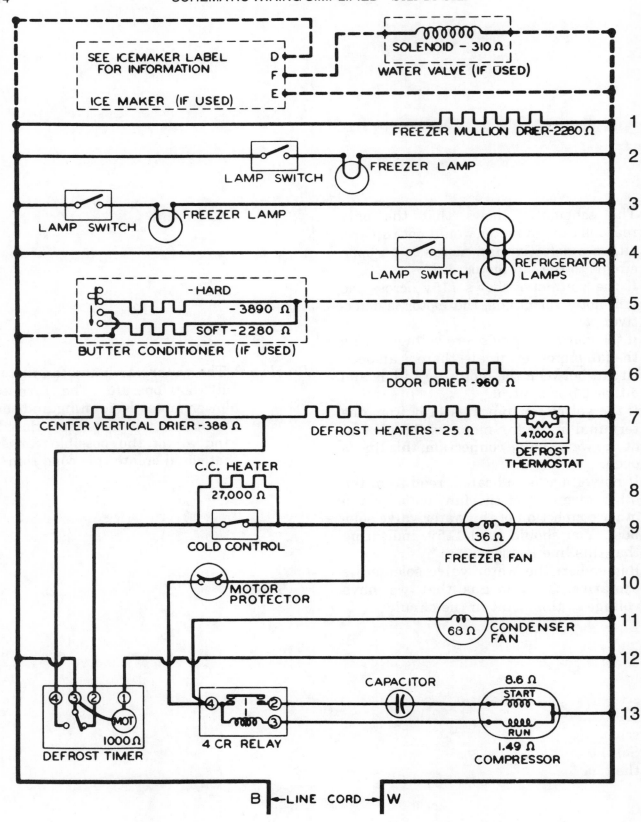

FRIGIDAIRE REFRIGERATOR/FREEZER

This 115v Frigidaire model has two separate freezer compartments and one refrigeration section with automatic defrosting. A butter conditioner and an icemaker, with its water valve, are optional with this model.

The schematic supplied by Frigidaire is unique in that it gives the resistance across all motors, heater coils, and the compressor windings. To the service mechanic, they can be a very helpful tool in troubleshooting an electrical problem.

1. GO STEP-BY-STEP

THROUGH THE ELECTRICAL SEQUENCE

The easiest way to determine *what happens next* is to first eliminate the circuits that have no effect on the operation of the cooling or defrosting system.

To help in locating each device, we have numbered each of the parallel circuits down the side of the schematic. Starting from the top, the first circuit, in dotted lines, shows the field wiring connections for an automatic ice maker and its solenoid water valve.

- Line 1 shows a heater, called a freezer mullion drier ⎓⎓⎓⎓ MULLION DRIER , connected between B and W. (A mullion heater is used to prevent condensation forming on the strip of cabinet separating two doors. This strip is called a mullion.) The schematic shows no switches or controls. So, the mullion drier should be warm to the touch at all times.

- Line 2 shows a normally open door switch ⌀⌀ in series with the lamp ⏀ in the upper freezer compartment. The switch will close when the door is opened, completing a circuit to the freezer lamp from B to W.

- Line 3 shows another normally open door switch controlling the lamp in the lower freezer section.

- Line 4 shows a third normally open door switch controlling two lamps in the refrigerator section. The lamps are in series with the door switch and are wired in parallel with each other.

- Line 5 shows the field wiring for an optional butter conditioner. The butter conditioner consists of two electric resistance heaters, each with a different heat output. This added heat will hold the butter at a spreadable temperature. The slide switch has three positions:

1. ⌇⎓⎓⎓ 2. ⌇⎓⎓⎓ 3. ⌇⎓⎓⎓

1. In the *hard* or off position, there is no heat added.
2. The center position completes a circuit from B, through the 3890 ohm heater, to W.
3. In the *soft* position, a circuit is completed from B, through the 2280 ohm heater, to W.

- Line 6 shows a resistance heater , called a door drier ⎓⎓⎓⎓ DOOR DRIER , which is used to keep the freezer door clear of condensation. The heater is wired from B to W, with no *on* or *off* control.

We have now disposed of all the circuits that have no effect on the cooling and defrosting cycles.

• Line 7 shows four resistors: the 388 ohm center vertical drier, a pair of defrost heaters, totaling 25 ohms, and a 47,000 ohm resistor in the defrost thermostat [⎓]. Actually, the 47,000 ohm resistor has no functional purpose in this circuit. It is only there to permit continuity testing through the defrost thermostat. From now on, assume it is not in the circuit.

The defrost thermostat senses the temperature in the refrigerator cooling coil and will close when the temperature of the cooling coil is below freezing. With the cooling coil below freezing, frost can build up on the coil and in the freezer compartments.

When the thermostat closes, it completes the circuit to the drier and the defrost heaters. The total heat output is 32 watts, with 30 watts being concentrated at the center vertical drier. This small amount of heat prevents the formation of frost and ice at the door seals. The remaining heat, from the two defrost heaters, is of no consequence.

The system remains in this condition until the defrost timer motor [⎓], Line 13, advances to the defrost position. The motor runs constantly since it is connected, at timer terminals 1 and 3, to an uninterrupted circuit running along Line 12. The motor is programmed, by the manufacturer, to start and stop the defrost cycle by closing and opening a circuit between terminals 3 and 4 in the timer.

When terminals 3 and 4 are connected, to initiate the defrost cycle, an alternate circuit is completed from B, at Line 12, to a junction between the center vertical drier and the two defrost heaters on Line 7, thereby bypassing the center vertical drier which will not be needed while defrosting. With the 388 ohm resistor no longer in series, the two defrost heaters will now produce 530 watts. Defrosting will continue until the defrost timer interrupts the circuit or until the defrost thermostat senses that the cooling coil is above freezing and opens. This interrupts the circuit to the two defrost heaters, thereby guarding against overheating the freezer compartment during the defrost period.

At the conclusion of the defrost period, the defrost timer opens the circuit between terminals 3 and 4 and completes the circuit between terminals 2 and 3.

• Line 8 shows a cold control heater [C.C. HEATER 27,000 Ω] that is energized when the defrost timer switches to complete a circuit from B, at Line 12, through terminals 2 and 3. This heater warms the bellows of the cold control thermostat [⎓], Line 9, to assure that the temperature is read at the sensing probe and not at the bellows.

- Line 9 shows the cold control thermostat and the freezer fan 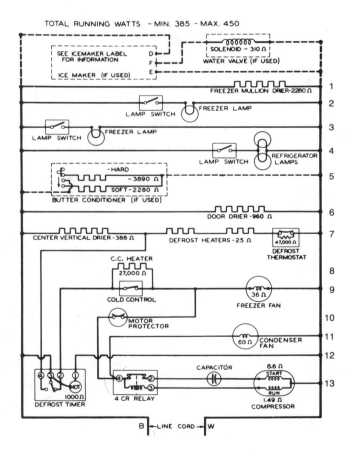 wired in series. They operate on the same circuit as the cold control heater.

  With the cold control open, the voltage drop across the cold control heater consumes virtually all the available voltage. Consequently, the freezer fan will not operate.

  When the cold control is closed, calling for refrigeration, the cold control heater is bypassed and the freezer fan, mounted near the cooling coil, will circulate cold air through all compartments of the refrigerator.

  With the cold control switch closed, a parallel circuit is completed through the motor protector, Line 10, to terminal 4 of the compressor relay, Line 13. (On some current relays, terminal 4 is marked L.)

  Simultaneously, another parallel circuit is completed from terminal 4 of the CR relay to the condenser fan on Line 11.

- Line 13 shows a circuit completed from terminal 4 in the CR relay, through the relay coil, to terminal 3 and through the compressor run winding to W. With the relay coil energized, the contacts close, completing a circuit, through terminal 2, to the capacitor and the compressor start winding. (On some current relays, terminals 2 and 3 will be marked S and M.) When the compressor is nearly up to speed, the relay will open and take the start winding out of the system.

The compressor will continue to run as long as the cold control remains closed, calling for refrigeration, or until the defrost timer advances to the defrost cycle, thereby opening terminals 2 to 3 in the timer and closing terminals 3 to 4.

During the defrost cycle, the center vertical drier will again be bypassed and the defrost thermostat will initiate defrosting when it senses temperatures below 32 °F.

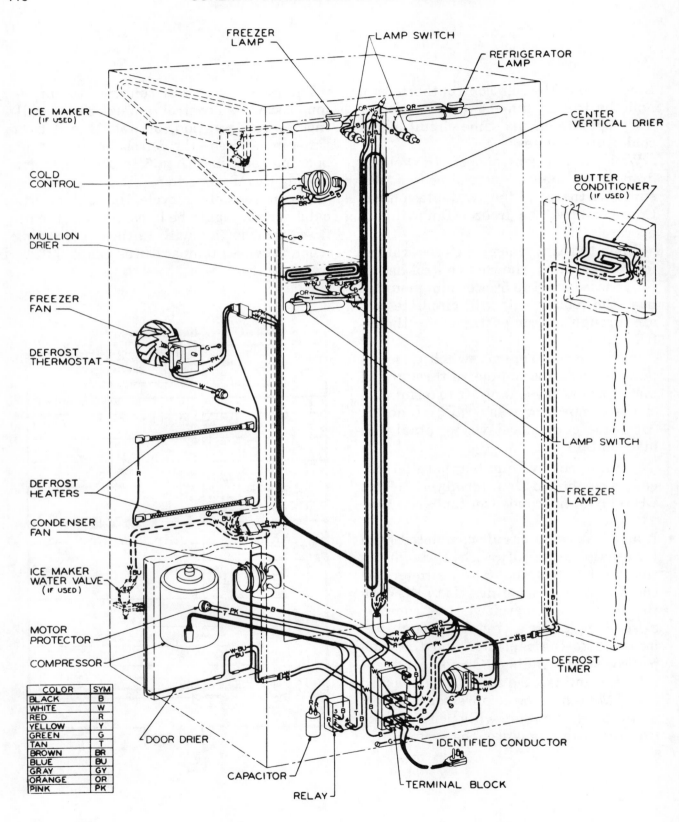

COLOR	SYM
BLACK	B
WHITE	W
RED	R
YELLOW	Y
GREEN	G
TAN	T
BROWN	BR
BLUE	BU
GRAY	GY
ORANGE	OR
PINK	PK

FREEZER LAMP

LAMP SWITCH

REFRIGERATOR LAMP

ICE MAKER (IF USED)

CENTER VERTICAL DRIER

COLD CONTROL

BUTTER CONDITIONER (IF USED)

MULLION DRIER

FREEZER FAN

DEFROST THERMOSTAT

LAMP SWITCH

FREEZER LAMP

DEFROST HEATERS

CONDENSER FAN

ICE MAKER WATER VALVE (IF USED)

MOTOR PROTECTOR

COMPRESSOR

DEFROST TIMER

DOOR DRIER

IDENTIFIED CONDUCTOR

CAPACITOR

TERMINAL BLOCK

RELAY

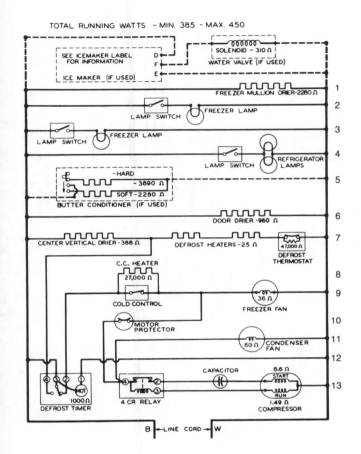

TOTAL RUNNING WATTS – MIN. 385 - MAX. 450

What voltages would you expect to read across the following motors, heaters and switches; first in the cooling cycle and then in the defrost cycle:

1. Freezer mullion drier, Line 1
2. Door drier, Line 6
3. Center vertical drier, Line 7
4. Defrost heaters, Line 7
5. Cold control heater, Line 8
6. Freezer fan, Line 9
7. Condenser fan, Line 11
8. Defrost timer motor, terminals 1 to 3, Line 13
9. Common to run on the compressor, Line 13
10. Cold control, Line 9
11. Motor protector, Line 10

Solve these problems using the five-step procedure.

Problem 1. Refrigerator will not defrost.

Problem 2. Refrigerator will not come out of defrost.

Problem 3. Compressor will not start and run. There is no hum at the compressor. Condenser fan and freezer fan are working.

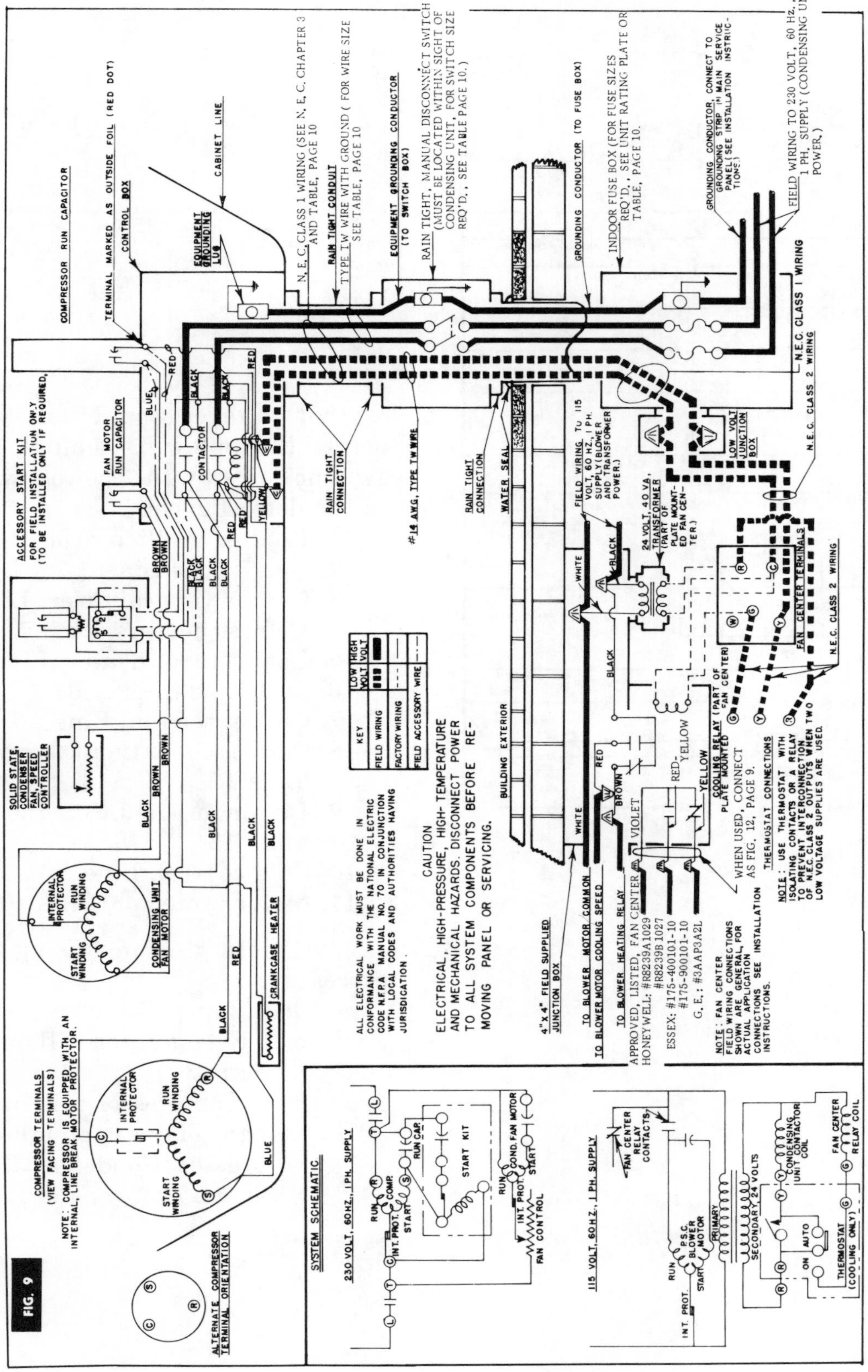
WIRING DIAGRAMS HEIL CONDENSING UNIT MODELS CU325AQD-1C,
CU329AQD-1T, CU336AQD-1C, CU342AQD-1T, CU348AQD-1C AND CU355AQD-1C
FIG. 9
ALTERNATE COMPRESSOR TERMINAL ORIENTATION
COMPRESSOR TERMINALS (VIEW FACING TERMINALS)
NOTE: COMPRESSOR IS EQUIPPED WITH AN INTERNAL, LINE BREAK MOTOR PROTECTOR.
CONDENSING UNIT FAN MOTOR
CRANKCASE HEATER
SOLID STATE CONDENSER FAN SPEED CONTROLLER
ACCESSORY START KIT FOR FIELD INSTALLATION ONLY (TO BE INSTALLED ONLY IF REQUIRED)
FAN MOTOR RUN CAPACITOR
CONTACTOR
COMPRESSOR RUN CAPACITOR
TERMINAL MARKED AS OUTSIDE FOIL (RED DOT)
CONTROL BOX
CABINET LINE
EQUIPMENT GROUNDING LUG
N. E. C. CLASS 1 WIRING (SEE N. E. C. CHAPTER 3 AND TABLE, PAGE 10
RAIN TIGHT CONDUIT
TYPE TW WIRE WITH GROUND (FOR WIRE SIZE SEE TABLE, PAGE 10
EQUIPMENT GROUNDING CONDUCTOR (TO SWITCH BOX)
RAIN TIGHT, MANUAL DISCONNECT SWITCH (MUST BE LOCATED WITHIN SIGHT OF CONDENSING UNIT, FOR SWITCH SIZE REQ'D., SEE TABLE PAGE 10.)
GROUNDING CONDUCTOR (TO FUSE BOX)
INDOOR FUSE BOX (FOR FUSE SIZES REQ'D., SEE UNIT RATING PLATE OR TABLE, PAGE 10.
GROUNDING CONDUCTOR, CONNECT TO GROUNDING STRIP IN MAIN SERVICE PANEL (SEE INSTALLATION INSTRUCTIONS)
FIELD WIRING TO 230 VOLT, 60 Hz., 1 PH. SUPPLY (CONDENSING UNIT POWER.)
N.E.C. CLASS 1 WIRING
N.E.C. CLASS 2 WIRING
LOW VOLT JUNCTION BOX
RAIN TIGHT CONNECTION
#14 AWG. TYPE TW WIRE
WATER SEAL
BUILDING EXTERIOR
KEY
LOW VOLT
HIGH VOLT
FIELD WIRING
FACTORY WIRING
FIELD ACCESSORY WIRE
ALL ELECTRICAL WORK MUST BE DONE IN CONFORMANCE WITH THE NATIONAL ELECTRIC CODE N.F.P.A. MANUAL NO. 70 IN CONJUNCTION WITH LOCAL CODES AND AUTHORITIES HAVING JURISDICATION.
CAUTION
ELECTRICAL, HIGH-PRESSURE, HIGH-TEMPERATURE AND MECHANICAL HAZARDS. DISCONNECT POWER TO ALL SYSTEM COMPONENTS BEFORE REMOVING PANEL OR SERVICING.
FIELD WIRING TO 115 VOLT, 60 HZ., 1 PH. SUPPLY (BLOWER AND TRANSFORMER POWER.)
24 VOLT, 40 VA. TRANSFORMER (PART OF PLATE MOUNTED FAN CENTER.)
FAN CENTER TERMINALS
COOLING RELAY (PART OF PLATE MOUNTED FAN CENTER)
4" x 4" FIELD SUPPLIED JUNCTION BOX
TO BLOWER MOTOR COMMON
TO BLOWER MOTOR COOLING SPEED
TO BLOWER HEATING RELAY
APPROVED, LISTED, FAN CENTER HONEYWELL: #R8239A1029 #R8239B1027
ESSEX: #175-400101-10 #175-900101-10
G. E.: #3AAP3A2L
WHEN USED, CONNECT AS FIG. 12, PAGE 9.
NOTE: FAN CENTER FIELD WIRING CONNECTIONS SHOWN ARE GENERAL, FOR ACTUAL APPLICATION CONNECTIONS SEE INSTALLATION INSTRUCTIONS.
THERMOSTAT CONNECTIONS
NOTE: USE THERMOSTAT WITH ISOLATING CONTACTS OR A RELAY TO PREVENT INTERCONNECTION OF N.E.C. CLASS 2 OUTPUTS WHEN TWO LOW VOLTAGE SUPPLIES ARE USED.
SYSTEM SCHEMATIC
230 VOLT, 60HZ., 1PH. SUPPLY
START KIT
RUN CAP.
COND. FAN MOTOR
FAN CONTROL
115 VOLT, 60HZ., 1PH. SUPPLY
FAN CENTER RELAY CONTACTS
P.S.C. BLOWER MOTOR
PRIMARY
SECONDARY 24 VOLTS
CONDENSING UNIT CONTACTOR COIL
FAN CENTER RELAY COIL
THERMOSTAT (COOLING ONLY)

Heil-Quaker Air Conditioning Condensing Unit

Reading from top to bottom, the schematic for the Heil-Quaker condensing unit shows the high-voltage (230v) outside wiring, 115v furnace wiring, and the 24v control wiring. The condensing unit contactor coil, shown on the 24v inside wiring schematic, is actually located in the outside condensing unit. Field wiring ——— , from the thermostat, is run to the contactor coil.

With an add-on system, an *A coil*, or cooling coil, is installed in the plenum of a hot-air furnace. The wiring to the outside condensing unit includes both a 230v and a 24v circuit.

For this example, we will only cover the condensing unit.

Please note that the thermostat shown in the schematic is incorrectly wired. Oversights of this type are not unusual in schematics, especially when the component is to be field installed. The correct wiring is shown in Section VI.

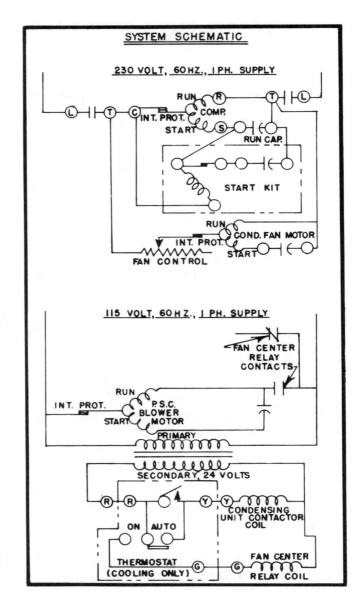

1. GO STEP-BY-STEP
THROUGH THE ELECTRICAL SEQUENCE

To determine *what happens next*, set the thermostat selector to COOL, the fan switch ON|AUTO to AUTO, and lower the thermostat setting below room temperature to close contacts ⓡ to ⓨ.

- With contacts R to Y closed, a circuit is completed from the 24v transformer secondary SECONDARY 24 VOLTS and through the condensing unit contactor coil CONDENSING UNIT CONTACTOR.

- Since the fan control contacts ON|AUTO have been manually closed, the indoor fan relay coil FAN CENTER is energized whenever the thermostat contacts close for cooling. This assures that the indoor fan will run whenever the compressor starts. With the indoor fan relay coil energized, the normally-open fan center relay contacts FAN CENTER close, completing a circuit, through the internal protector INT. PROT., to the permanent split capacitor (PSC) blower motor.

- When the condensing unit contactor coil CONDENSING UNIT CONTACTOR is energized, the normally open contacts, ⓛ─┤├─ⓣ and ⓣ─┤├─ⓛ, in the 230v circuit, close, completing two parallel circuits.

- One circuit, from T to T on the contactor, goes through the solid state condenser fan speed control FAN CONTROL. The speed control matches the speed of the condenser fan motor to the outside air temperature. As the outside temperature increases, the condenser fan will run faster. A decrease in outside air temperature will slow the fan motor. The speed control will automatically vary the fan speed when the outdoor air temperature is below 105 °F and above 75 °F.

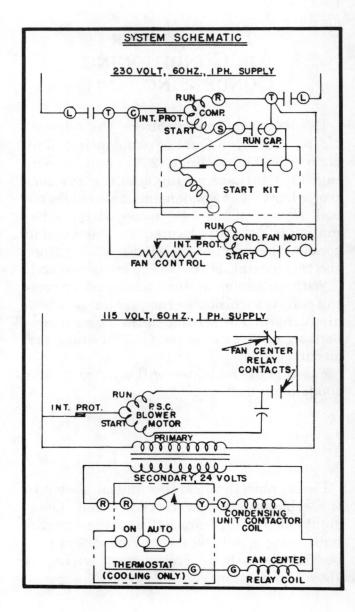

SYSTEM SCHEMATIC

230 VOLT, 60 HZ., 1 PH. SUPPLY

115 VOLT, 60 HZ., 1 PH. SUPPLY

- From the speed control, the circuit continues through the internal protector to the common of the condenser fan motor ⟨symbol⟩. Even though the internal protector is schematically shown outside of the fan motor, it is located inside the motor and connected between the outside terminal of the motor and the common junction of the start and run windings.
- With the contactor contacts closed, a second circuit is completed through the internal protector to the common in the compressor ⟨symbol⟩.
- This compressor has a permanent split capacitor motor (PSC) with a run capacitor ⟨symbol⟩. The schematic shows where to wire a hard-start kit, if required.

The hard-start kit, shown inside the dotted line, consists of a potential start relay ⟨symbol⟩ and a start capacitor ⟨symbol⟩. The kit is used to overcome hard starting in areas where voltages are below normal.

Observing the condenser schematic:
- The condensing unit contactor controls the operation of both the compressor and the condenser fan motor.
- The condenser fan motor can operate without the compressor and the compressor can operate without the fan motor. This can only happen if one of the motors is defective.
- So long as there is 24v to the condensing unit contactor coil, the condensing unit fan and compressor can operate.

Set the thermostat to start the system. Using a voltmeter, what voltages would you expect to read across the following motors, contacts and coils:
 1. ⓡ to ⓒ on the compressor
 2. RUN to common on the condenser fan motor
 3. Ⓛ to Ⓣ on the contactor
 4. ⓡ to Ⓨ on the thermostat
 5. ⓡ to Ⓨ on the condensing unit contactor coil
 6. Primary of transformer

Using the five-step procedure, solve these three problems:

Problem 1. Condenser fan does not run. Compressor is running.
Problem 2. Condenser fan and compressor are not running. Blower motor is operating.
Problem 3. Condenser fan, compressor and blower motor will not run.

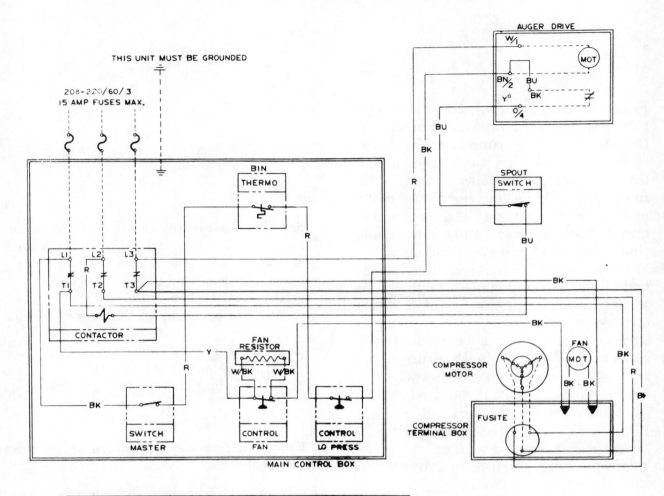

ALL CONTROLS SHOWN IN NORMAL ICE MAKING MODE

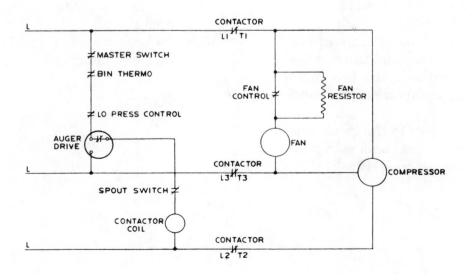

SCOTSMAN COMMERCIAL ICE FLAKER

This Scotsman ice flaker delivers a high volume and continuous flow of flaked ice to the storage bin.

Like most ice makers, the flaker will continue to make ice until the bin is full or the master switch is opened. The bin thermostat sensing element, mounted near the top of the bin, is set to open the thermostat contacts at approximately 32 °F, the temperature of ice, and shut down the system. If ice is constantly removed from the bin, the flaker will continue to make ice.

1. GO STEP-BY-STEP
THROUGH THE ELECTRICAL SEQUENCE

The wiring diagram shows the compressor to be 208/220v, 3φ, 60 Hz. The condenser fan motor, auger motor and compressor contactor coil are 208/220v, 1φ, 60 Hz. Since the schematic is rudimentary, showing all switches as ≠, we will amplify this information by showing the graphics from the wiring diagram while following the schematic.

All contacts are in the operating or ice-making position, even though the normal position of some contacts, such as the low pressure switch ⊥, contactor contacts ≠, fan control ⊥, and master switch ⊸ is open.

- To start the ice machine, the manually-operated master switch ⊸ must be closed, initiating a circuit from L1 through the master switch to the bin thermostat ⊥.

- The bin thermostat, which opens on a temperature fall, would be closed at this time, permitting the circuit to continue to the low pressure control ⊥.

- The low pressure control serves two purposes. First, it will shut down the system if the temperature and, thus, the pressure of the refrigerant in the evaporator drops too low. This drop could be due to a loss of water, which is the heat load on the evaporator. A drop in evaporator pressure could cause the turning auger to freeze, with possible damage to the auger drive and the auger, itself.

  Second, because the compressor will continue to operate until the bin thermostat opens, a loss of refrigerant will keep the compressor running even though no ice is being produced. The low pressure switch will open if there is a loss of refrigerant.

- From the low pressure control, the control circuit runs through a normally closed motor protector switch ⟳, that protects the auger motor.

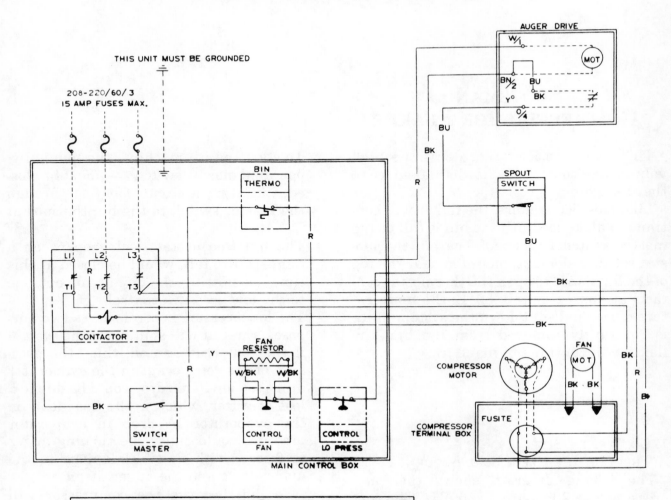

ALL CONTROLS SHOWN IN NORMAL ICE MAKING MODE

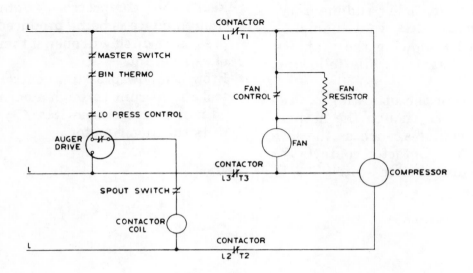

- The circuit continues through the normally closed spout switch ⎯•⎯. The spout switch is a mechanically-operated safety that will open if ice builds up in the spout, pushing the switch open.
- From the spout switch, the circuit energizes the compressor contactor coil ⎯◠⎯, and terminates at L2.
- The auger drive motor ⊙, wired from L1 to L3, is controlled by the master switch ⎯•⎯, bin thermostat ⌐, and low pressure control ⌐ and will continue to run if the spout switch is open, or an open contactor coil failed to close the contactor contacts.
- With the compressor contactor contacts closed, L1≠T1, L2≠T2, L3≠T3, the three-phase compressor ⊛ will start. However, the compressor will not start if either the master switch, bin thermostat, low-pressure control, auger overload or spout switch is open. The control circuit is a series circuit.
- The condenser fan motor (FAN MOT), wired between T1 and T3, will run when the compressor contactor is closed. This is to guarantee that the condenser fan and compressor operate together.
- Between T1 and the condenser fan motor is a fan control ⌐, and a fan resistor ⎯◠◠◠⎯ that is wired parallel to the fan control. The fan control is a low pressure switch that makes on an increase in head pressure. If the air temperature at the condenser is low, the fan control will be open and the fan will be energized through the fan resistor, causing the fan to run at a low speed. When the air temperature increases, the head pressure will rise, closing the fan control. The condenser fan will now run at high speed.

Observing the schematic: If fuse L2 ⌁ is out, the auger motor will still operate. If fuse L3 is out, the contactor will pull in, but the compressor, condenser fan, and auger will not start. If fuse L1 is out, nothing will start.

What voltages would you expect to read across the following switches, motors and coils, with the system operating on a primary voltage of 220v/3φ.

1. Master switch
2. Bin thermostat
3. Low pressure control
4. Spout switch
5. Fan control (motor at low speed)
6. Fan motor (motor at high speed)
7. Auger motor
8. Contactor coil

Using the five-step procedure, solve the following problems.

Problem 1. Fan motor will not operate. Compressor and auger motor running.

Problem 2. Compressor and fan not starting. Auger motor running.

Problem 3. Nothing operating. 220v at L1, L2, L3.

ARKLA
AIR-COOLED CHILLER

The Arkla air-cooled chiller is an ammonia/water absorption refrigeration system, using natural or LP gas as the heat source for the generator. Electricity performs a supportive role by operating the controls, gas valve, chilled water pump and the solution pump.

The absorption chiller removes heat from recirculated water. The chilled water, at about 45 °F, is then circulated through a remote blower coil. Return air is drawn across the coil, giving up heat to the chilled water. The cooler air is discharged into the conditioned space and the warm water, at about 55 °F, is returned to the chiller.

The wiring diagram appears to be loaded with controls. The schematic, shows only a few necessary electrical devices. The chiller comes completely factory wired, except for the low voltage thermostat. Primary voltage, supplied to L1 and L2, is 230v, 1φ, 50 or 60 Hz.

1. GO STEP-BY-STEP
THROUGH THE ELECTRICAL SEQUENCE

Set the thermostat selector to *cool* and fan on *auto*. (The thermostat and the indoor fan circuit are not shown on this schematic. The fan will start when the thermostat contacts close for cooling.) Lower the thermostat temperature setting below room temperature to complete the circuit from ⓡ to ⓨ.

- With R to Y closed, a circuit is completed from the transformer secondary ⬚⬚ to the heater ᴏⱳᴏ in the time delay switch ⬚ and, from there, to the high temperature switch ⬚. The high temperature switch is a limit switch that prevents overheating.

- After approximately 45 seconds, the time delay heater will close the time delay switch ⬚ and energize the relay coil ⬚.

- With the relay coil energized, the relay contacts ⬚ in the 230v circuit will close and start both the chilled water pump motor ⊖⊖(split phase, capacitor start) and the condenser fan motor ⬚ (permanent split capacitor).

- With the fan operating, air movement will close the normally-open sail switch ⬚ and complete a parallel circuit, through the normally-closed chilled water switch ⬚ to the gas valve ⬚ in the 24v system.

The purpose of the sail switch is to prevent overheating by assuring that the condenser fan is providing vent and draft for the burner.

The purpose of the chilled water switch is to prevent freeze-up if the water is not being circulated. This switch opens at 38 °F, stopping the absorption cycle, and resets at 42 °F.

- With the circuit completed to the gas valve, the burner can be ignited and the absorption refrigeration cycle begins.

- If the thermostat opens or one of the safety switches opens, there will be no voltage to either the gas valve circuit or the time delay switch heater. However, residual heat from the heater will hold the time delay switch closed for approximately 3½ minutes during which the pump and fan will continue to operate. When the time delay switch has cooled, the switch will open and all circuits will be de-energized.

Set the thermostat selector to *cool*, fan to *auto,* and lower temperature setting to close R to Y. After 45 seconds, what voltages would you expect to read across the following motors, coils and switches?

1. Relay contacts
2. Time delay contacts
3. Sail switch
4. Chilled water switch
5. Hi-temperature switch
6. Gas valve coil
7. Time delay relay coil
8. Relay coil
9. Pump motor
10. Run to common on fan motor

Using the five-step procedure, solve these problems:

Problem 1. Gas valve will not open, pilot is on.

Problem 2. Fan and pump will not start.

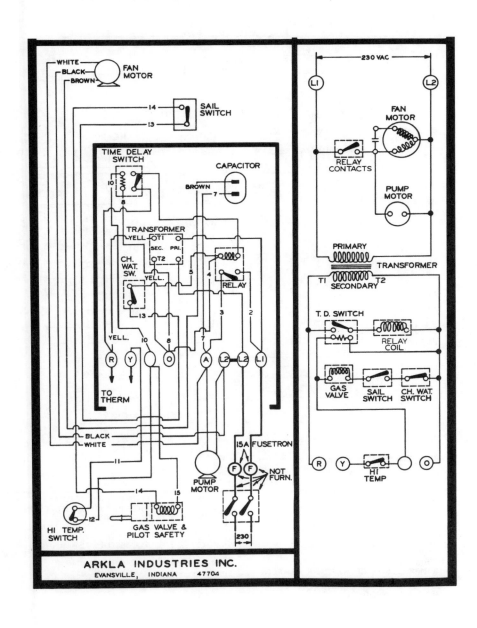

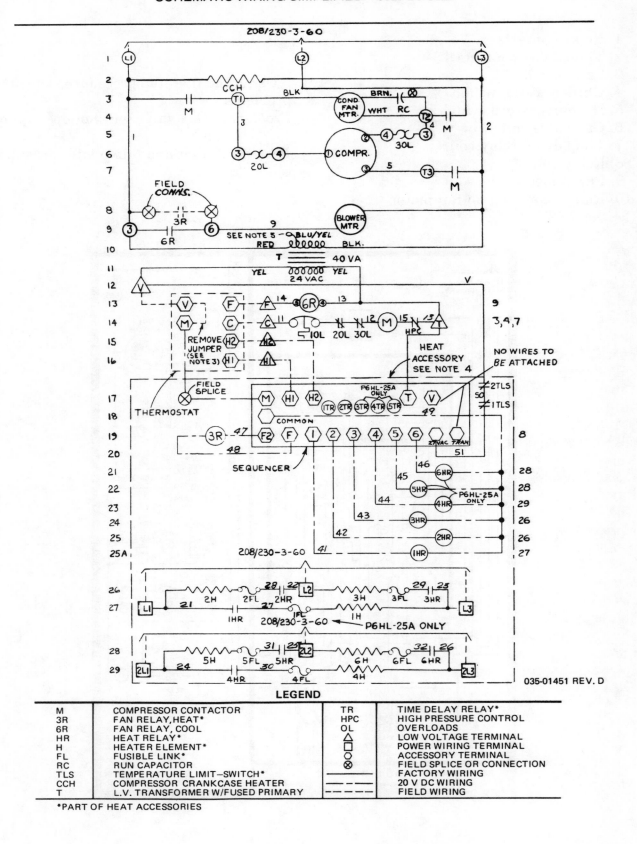

LEGEND

M	COMPRESSOR CONTACTOR	TR	TIME DELAY RELAY*
3R	FAN RELAY, HEAT*	HPC	HIGH PRESSURE CONTROL
6R	FAN RELAY, COOL	OL	OVERLOADS
HR	HEAT RELAY*	△	LOW VOLTAGE TERMINAL
H	HEATER ELEMENT*	□	POWER WIRING TERMINAL
FL	FUSIBLE LINK*	◇	ACCESSORY TERMINAL
RC	RUN CAPACITOR	⊗	FIELD SPLICE OR CONNECTION
TLS	TEMPERATURE LIMIT—SWITCH*	——	FACTORY WIRING
CCH	COMPRESSOR CRANKCASE HEATER	— —	20 V DC WIRING
T	L.V. TRANSFORMER W/FUSED PRIMARY	– – –	FIELD WIRING

*PART OF HEAT ACCESSORIES

035-01451 REV. D

York
Package Air Conditioner
with
Electric Resistance Heat

The York schematic is a little different from the previous examples. Note that the numbers running down the left side of the schematic are for line reference only. The lines on the right side, however, indicate the lines on which the contacts for each relay are found.

For example, reading from the left across Line 14, you will find a relay coil ⓜ. Continuing across Line 14, to the right margin, you will find the notation 3, 4, 7, indicating that the contacts for relay M are found on Lines 3, 4 and 7.

The room thermostat for this unit should have separate heating and cooling circuits. The sequencer, used to bring in the heating coils, converts 24v ac to 20v dc and is equipped with heater relays, time delay relays and a fan relay, all operating on 20v direct current. The room thermostat jumper, between terminals ⓥ and ⓜ (Lines 13 and 14), must be removed. If not removed, it will short out ac to dc power and damage the sequencer. The thermostat may be either single-stage heat and single-stage cool or two-stage heat and single-stage cool.

Referring to the schematic, Lines 14, 15 and 16, the thermostat terminals ⓜ, ⑭², and ⑭¹ are dc and connected to the sequencer at Line 17. All wires numbered 41 through 51 are direct current. All other wires are alternating current.

The number of each wire is actually printed on the wire insulation. For instance: relay ③ₕ, found on Line 24, has its contacts on Line 26 and is connected to ③ on Line 19 by wire number 43.

The operation of the solid state heating sequencer will be discussed when we trace the heating cycle. First, we will trace the cooling system.

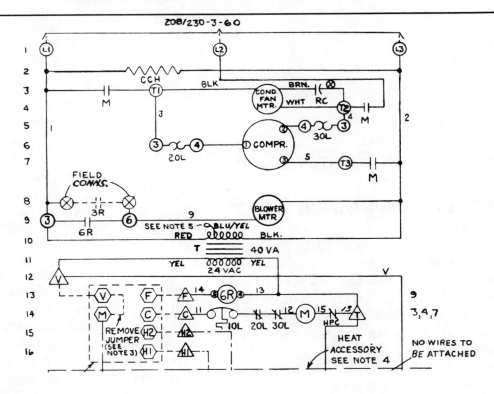

1. GO STEP-BY-STEP
THROUGH THE ELECTRICAL SEQUENCE.

COOLING CYCLE

- Place thermostat selector on *cool*, fan on *auto*. Lower the thermostat setting below room temperature to close contacts Ⓥ to Ⓒ, Line 13 to Line 14.
- With contacts Ⓥ to Ⓒ closed, a circuit is completed from △V, Line 12, to one side of the 24v transformer secondary ‾‾‾‾‾, 24VAC, Line 11, to △C, Line 14, the low voltage terminal in the package unit.
- From △C, the circuit continues, on Line 14, through the temperature-actuated overload ⌇, and the current actuated overloads ⌇ and ⌇, energizing the compressor contactor coil Ⓜ.
- The circuit from the compressor contactor coil is completed through the normally-closed high pressure control ⌇, to the low voltage terminal △T, the other side of the 24v transformer.

- When thermostat contacts Ⓥ–Ⓒ closed, the circuit through contacts Ⓥ–Ⓕ, Line 13, was energized, completing a circuit to terminal △F in the package unit.
- From △F, the circuit continues to the cooling fan relay coil ⑥R and back to the 24v transformer secondary.

Observing the low voltage cooling control circuit:

- The compressor contactor coil Ⓜ will de-energize if the overloads ⌇, ⌇, ⌇ or the high pressure switch ⌇, all on Line 14, open or the contacts V to C in the thermostat open.
- The cooling fan relay coil will de-energize only by opening contacts V to F in the thermostat.

Recheck the low voltage circuit before tracing the 3-phase high voltage circuit:

- Wired between L1 and L3, on Line 2, is a compressor crankcase heater $\sim\!\!\!\text{WWW}\!\!\!\sim_{\text{CCH}}$. Since there are no switches in the crankcase heater circuit, the heater is hot as long as there is 230v at L1 and L3.

- When compressor contactor coil (M) was energized, the margin note to the right of Line 14 indicated that the contacts $\dashv\vdash_{\text{M}}$ on Lines 3, 4, and 7 closed.

    Line 3 shows normally-open compressor contactor contacts $\dashv\vdash_{\text{M}}$. With these contacts closed, a circuit is completed from L1-T1 to the common terminal of the condenser fan motor (COND FAN MTR). The schematic indicates that the condenser fan motor is a permanent split capacitor (PSC), with a run capacitor $\dashv\vdash_{\text{RC}}$. A circuit is also run from L1-T1, through overload protector $\sim\!\!\!\!\text{x}_{\text{2OL}}$, to compressor terminal 1.

    Line 4 shows normally open contacts $\dashv\vdash_{\text{M}}$. When these contacts close, a circuit is run from L2-T2, to the run and start terminals of the condenser fan motor. A circuit is also completed from L2-T2, through an overload protector $\sim\!\!\!\!\text{x}_{\text{3OL}}$, to compressor terminal 2.

    Line 7 shows normally-open compressor contactor contacts $\dashv\vdash_{\text{M}}$. With these contacts closed, a circuit is completed from L3-T3 to terminal 3 on the compressor.

- The contacts $\dashv\vdash_{\text{6R}}$ on Line 9 close when the cooling fan relay coil (6R) is energized, completing a circuit to the blower motor (BLOWER MTR) from L1 to L3.

- The 208/230 step-down control circuit transformer $\sim\!\!\overline{\text{obooo}}^{\text{BLU/YEL}}$, Line 10, is wired hot from L1 to L3.

Observing the high voltage cooling control circuit:

- The condenser fan motor, wired between L1 and L2 will not run if fuse L3 is open. The fuses, which preceed L1, L2, and L3, are not shown. If L3 is open, the transformer, supplying voltage to coil (M), is de-energized.

- The blower motor, wired between L1 and L3, will run if fuse L2 is open.

- If L1, L2 or L3 is open, the compressor will not run.

- The control transformer and the crankcase heater, wired between L1 and L3, will operate if fuse L2 is open.

- In a 3-phase circuit, it is necessary to check each lead, L1, L2, and L3, with a voltmeter, before attacking a problem. It is easy to be fooled into thinking that the nonoperating motor or device is defective where, in reality, one of the fuses is open.

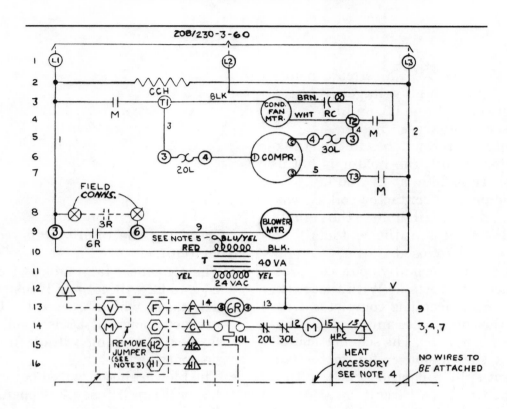

With the thermostat set on *cool,* the fan control on *auto,* to close contacts V—F, and the temperature setting lowered, to close contacts V—C, what voltages would you read across the following cooling side components:

1. Coil $\sim\!\!\sim\!\!\sim$ (Line 2)
2. Coil Ⓜ (Line 14)
3. Coil ⑥Ⓡ (Line 13)
4. Contacts $\frac{\dagger\dagger}{M}$ (Lines 3, 4, 7)
5. Contacts $\frac{\rightthreetimes}{HPC}$ (Line 14)
6. Contacts $\frac{\sigma\Lsh\sigma}{10L}$, $\frac{\rightthreetimes}{20L}$, $\frac{\rightthreetimes}{30L}$ (Line 14)
7. Contacts $\frac{\dagger\dagger}{6R}$ (Line 9)
8. Compressor Terminals 1 to 2, 2 to 3, 1 to 3
9. Condenser Fan Motor Terminals T1 to T2
10. Blower Motor Terminals

Solve these problems using the five-step procedure:

Problem 1. Blower motor will not run. Condenser fan motor and compressor are operating.

Problem 2. Condenser fan and compressor not running, blower motor operating.

Problem 3. Compressor not running. Condenser fan and blower motor running.

HEATING CYCLE

The electric heat accessory package for this unit is a solid state sequencer. This sequencer has several advantages, such as quiet operation, time delay between each heat strip, continued fan operation until all heater strips have been de-energized, and many staging possibilities.

The sequencer converts 24v ac to 20v dc. All relays contained in the sequencer are controlled by 20v direct current. It is essential that the proper thermostat be used, which has separate heat and cool circuits, to insure circuit isolation.

- ⟨M⟩, ⟨H2⟩, and ⟨HI⟩ on the thermostat are connected to terminals ⟨M⟩, ⟨H2⟩, and ⟨HI⟩ on the sequencer using 20v dc field wiring.

- ⟨A⟩, on one side of the 24v ac transformer, is factory-wired to terminal ⟨⟩ on the sequencer. Another wire from ⟨A⟩, the other side of the transformer, is factory-wired to terminal ⟨T⟩ on the sequencer. From terminals ⟨⟩ and ⟨T⟩, the sequencer converts the 24v ac to 20v dc. The 20v dc circuit is isolated from the 24v ac circuit by removing the jumper wire between ⟨V⟩ and ⟨M⟩ in the thermostat. It is necessary to use a dc voltmeter for checking the heating control circuit, and an ac voltmeter for checking the cooling circuit.

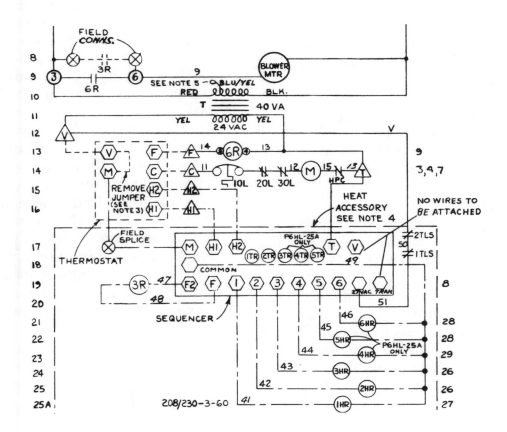

Set the thermostat selector on *heat,* fan on *auto,* and raise the temperature setting to close the first stage of heat contacts M to H1.

- With the contacts M to H1 closed, the 20v dc heating fan relay coil ③R (Line 19), wired from terminal ⟨F2⟩ to ⟨F⟩ on the sequencer, is energized. Contacts ⊣⊢3R (Line 8) close.
- At the same time, heat relay coil (1HR) (Line 25A), wired from ⟨I⟩ (Line 19) to common on the sequencer, is energized.
- The time delay relay coil (TR) (Line 18) is also energized.
- After about 10 seconds (minimum) of heating, the contacts in the time delay relay (TR) close. This completes the circuit to heat relay coil (2HR) (Line 25), and the time delay relay coil (2TR).
- Approximately 20 seconds (minimum) after the thermostat closed for heating, the contacts in the time delay relay (2TR) close, completing a circuit to heat relay coil (3HR) (Line 24).

  This sequencer has been staged for two stages of heat with 1HR, 2HR and 3HR on the first stage of heat H1. Heaters 4HR, 5HR and 6HR are on the second stage of heat H2. The time delay relay (3TR) has been removed for two-stage heating operation. A jumper wire (not shown) has been run from ⟨H2⟩ on the sequencer to the socket from which the (3TR) relay was removed.

- If the temperature around the thermostat drops another 1½° to 2°, contacts M to H2 close, and heat relay coil (4HR) (Line 23), is energized. At the same time, time delay relay coil (4TR) is energized.

- Approximately 10 seconds (minimum) later, the time delay relay contacts (4TR) close, energizing heater relay coil (5HR), and time delay relay coil (5TR).
- Approximately 10 seconds (minimum) later, the time delay relay contacts (5TR) close, energizing heater relay coil (6HR).
- When the temperature around the thermostat rises 1½° to 2°, the second stage heat contacts open, breaking contacts M to H2.
- With the contacts M to H2 open, the heater relay coils de-energize, in 10 second (minimum) intervals, in the same order in which they were energized, 4HR, 5HR, 6HR.
- When the temperature around the thermostat rises to the setting on the thermostat, contacts M to H1 open, de-energizing the heater relay coils, 1HR, 2HR, 3HR, in 10 second (minimum) intervals, in the same order in which they were energized.
- The system has *fan logic,* which means that the fan relay coil (Line 19), remains energized until all heater relay coils have been de-energized.
- Temperature limit switches ⧣2TLS and 1TLS, (Lines 17, 18) which are automatically reset, are mounted in the heating package, and open one leg of the 24v ac circuit to the sequencer, de-energizing the 20v dc circuit, cutting all power to the heating relays, time delay relays and the fan relay.

Recheck the low voltage, 20v dc circuit, until you understand the sequence. Then proceed to the high voltage circuit.

Set thermostat to *heat,* fan on *auto* and raise the temperature setting to close contacts M to H1.

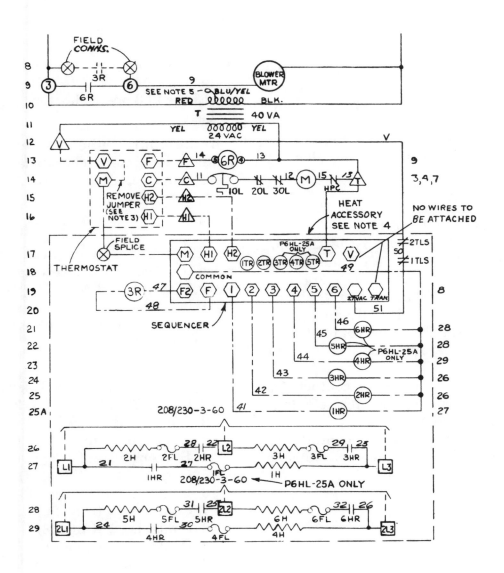

LINE VOLTAGE
- With contacts M to H1 closed, the heating fan relay coil ③R (Line 19), was energized, closing contacts ⊣⊢ 3R (Line 8) and completing a circuit to the blower motor (BLOWER MTR) from L1 to L3. Relay 3R is field installed and bypasses cooling fan contacts ⊣⊢ 6R.
- At the same time, heater relay coil 1HR was energized, closing contacts ⊣⊢ 1HR (Line 27) energizing heater element ∿∿∿ 1H between L1 and L3.
- Heater relay coil 2HR closes contacts ⊣⊢ 2HR (Line 26), energizing heater element ∿∿∿ 2H between L1 and L2.
- Heater relay coil 3HR closes contacts ⊣⊢ 3HR (Line 26), energizing heater element ∿∿∿ 3H, between L2 and L3.
- If the temperature around the thermostat drops another 1½° to 2°, the second stage contacts M to H2 close, energizing heater relay coil 4HR.
- With heater relay coil 4HR energized, contacts ⊣⊢ 4HR (Line 29) close, completing a circuit to heater element ∿∿∿ 4H from 2L1 to 2L3.
- Heater relay coil 5HR closes contacts ⊣⊢ 5HR (Line 28) energizing heater element ∿∿∿ 5H between 2L1 and 2L2.
- Heater relay coil 6HR closes contacts ⊣⊢ 6HR (Line 28), energizing heater element ∿∿∿ 6H between 2L2 and 2L3.

Examining the schematic:
- All heating elements are protected by a fusible link ⌢⌣ set to open at 333°F.
- If Line L1 opens, heater ∿∿∿ 3H will still heat.
- If Line L2 opens, heater ∿∿∿ 1H will still heat.
- If Line L3 opens, heater ∿∿∿ 2H will still heat.
- If Line 2L1 opens, heater ∿∿∿ 6H will still heat.
- If Line 2L2 opens, heater ∿∿∿ 4H will still heat.
- If Line 2L3 opens, heater ∿∿∿ 5H will still heat.

Remember, when troubleshooting 3-phase equipment, check the main voltage to terminals L1, L2, L3, 2L1, 2L2, and 2L3 first.

Set the thermostat on *heat*, fan on *auto*, raise the temperature setting to close contacts M to H1 and M to H2. Wait approximately 60 seconds for all heater elements to energize. Now, what voltages would you read across the following:

1. Coils 1HR, 2HR, 3HR, 4HR, 5HR, 6HR (Lines 25A, 25, 24, 23, 22, 21)
2. Coil ③R (Line 19)
3. Heater element ∿∿∿ 3H (Line 26)
4. Heater element ∿∿∿ 5H (Line 28)
5. Contacts ≠2TLS (Line 17)
6. Contacts ≠1TLS (Line 18)
7. Contacts ⊣⊢ 2HR (Line 26)
8. Contacts ⊣⊢ 6HR (Line 28)
9. Contacts ⊣⊢ 3R (Line 8)
10. Blower Motor Terminals (Lines 8, 9)

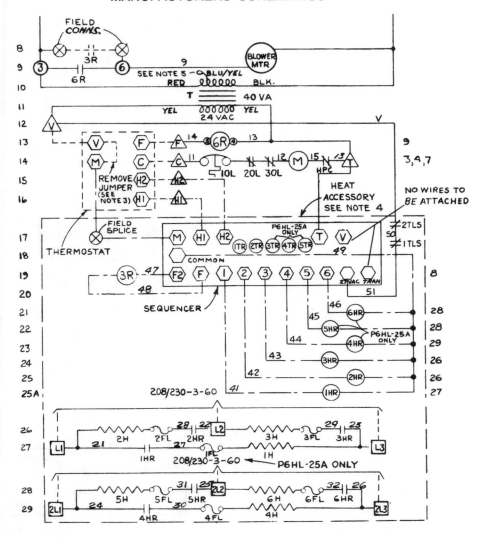

Using the five-step procedure, solve the following problems:

Problem 1. Heater elements 4H, 5H, 6H do not heat. Heater elements 1H, 2H, 3H and the blower motor are working.

Problem 2. Heater elements 2H, 3H do not heat. Heater elements 1H, 4H, 5H, 6H and the blower motor are working.

Problem 3. Blower motor does not come on. All heaters are energized.

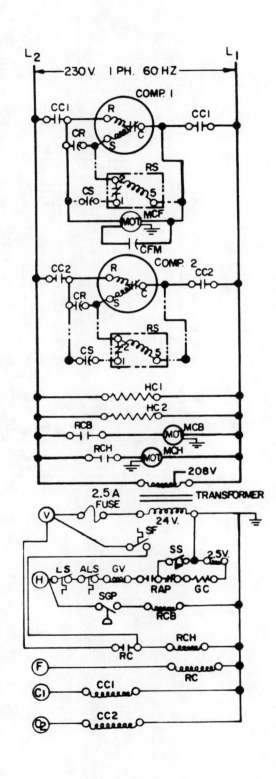

FEDDERS
ROOFTOP GAS HEATING AND
ELECTRIC COOLING PACKAGE

This commercial-size, 72,000 Btu rooftop package will heat or cool, automatically, from a field-wired, low voltage, two-stage cooling, one-stage heating thermostat. The schematic does not show the low voltage thermostat, but does indicate the terminals where the low voltage wires are field connected. Terminal V is to the fused side of the transformer secondary, terminal H is to the heating control circuit, terminal F is to the evaporator blower, terminals $C1$ and $C2$ are to the control circuits for compressor 1 and compressor 2.

1. GO STEP-BY-STEP
THROUGH THE ELECTRICAL SEQUENCE

COOLING CYCLE

Set the thermostat on *cool,* fan on *auto.* Lower the thermostat setting to energize the first stage, but not the second stage, of cooling. 230v will be present at L_1 and L_2.

- With the thermostat closed, first stage only, a circuit is completed from the 24v secondary of the transformer through the fuse to V and to $C1$. 24v will now energize the compressor contactor coil CC1 and complete the circuit back to the other side of the transformer secondary.

- If the temperature at the thermostat rises another 1½° to 2°, the second stage of the thermostat will close, completing a circuit from V to $C2$. 24v will energize the compressor contactor coil CC2 and complete the circuit to the other side of the transformer secondary.

- When the thermostat calls for cooling, a circuit from V is automatically completed through the thermostat fan selector to F. 24v will energize the cooling relay coil RC and complete the circuit to the transformer secondary.

- With coil RC energized, the normally open contacts RC in the 24v circuit will close, energizing the cooling-heating blower relay coil RCH from V, and complete this circuit to the transformer secondary.

From this information, we can see that if coil CC_1 is defective, coil CC_2 and coil RC can still function. With parallel circuits, each circuit operates independently and is not affected by the defects in the others. In the schematic, it can be seen that the coils CC_1, CC_2 and RC are controlled only by the thermostat.

Further observation will show that the blower relay coil RCH is controlled by the closing of contacts RC. However, coil RCH can also be energized by the closing of the temperature activated fan switch, on a rise in temperature, thereby completing a circuit from V that bypasses the fan switch. The fan switch is closed in the heating cycle to start the blower motor. It can be seen that a defective cooling relay coil RC will not start the blower on the cooling cycle, but the blower could operate during the heating cycle.

Recheck the low voltage circuit and proceed to the high voltage section of the schematic.

- From L_1, a wire is connected to the line side of one set of normally open contacts CC1 on the compressor contactor. L_2 is connected to the other set of normally open contacts CC1 on the compressor contactor.

- From the schematic, it can be seen that compressors 1 and 2 have internally protected IP, split phase, capacitor start CS, capacitor run CR motors, using a potential start relay RS covered in Section II.

- With coil CC_1 energized, contacts CC_1 and CC_1 close, starting compressor 1, through the start relay RS.

- When contacts CC_1 and CC_1 close, they also energize the condenser fan motor MCF. The schematic shows the condenser fan motor as a permanent split capacitor motor, showing only a run capacitor CFM and no start relay.

- On a call for the second stage of cooling C2 is also closed, energizing coil CC_2, thus closing the normally open contacts CC2 and CC2, starting compressor 2.

- Compressor heaters HC1 and HC2, also called crankcase heaters, have no switch to operate them. They are connected hot from L_1 to L_2.

- With contacts RC closed, the blower relay coil RCH in the 24v circuit is energized, closing the normally-open contacts RCH in the high voltage circuit, completing a circuit from L_1 through the blower motor MC1 to L_2, starting the evaporator blower.

As an electrical troubleshooter, it is important to take notice of the MCF circuit. The schematic shows that the condenser fan motor starts with the first stage of cooling. The MCF motor is parallel to compressor 1 and in series with the compressor contactor contacts CC_1 and CC_1. If the CC_1 coil in the low voltage circuit fails, and the CC_2 coil is good, compressor 2 will operate, but compressor 1 and the condenser fan motor will not operate, causing excessive compressor pressure. The schematic does not show a high pressure safety control that would shut down the compressor when the compressor pressure goes up. In this system, compressor 2 will cycle on and off, as the internal protector IP in the compressor opens and closes.

- The step-down transformer used has either a 230v or 208v primary connected hot from L_1 to L_2. The secondary has both a 24v lead for operation of all low voltage controls and a 2.5v lead to operate the glow coil GC in the heating circuit.

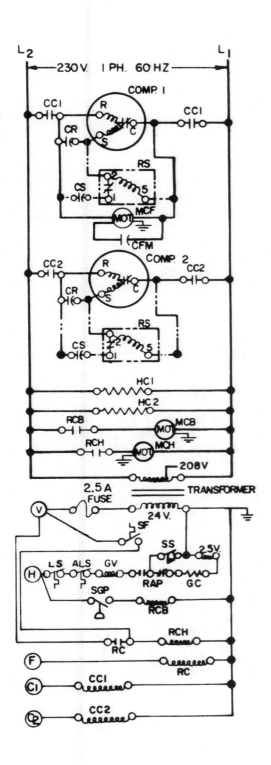

This completes the cooling side of the schematic. With the thermostat in the *cool* position, fan on *auto* and both stages of cooling closed, what voltages would be read, on a voltmeter, across the following switches, coils and motors:

1. Coil CC1
2. Coil CC2
3. Coil RC
4. Coil RCH
5. Coil HC1
6. Contacts RC
7. Contacts RCH
8. Contacts CC1
9. Contacts CC2
10. Motor MCB
11. Motor MCH

Using the 5-step procedure, solve these three problems:

Problem 1. Second stage compressor 2 does not come on. Compressor 1 and the condenser fan are operating. The evaporator blower is working.

Problem 2. Compressor 1 does not run. Compressor 2 does operate. Condenser fan operates. Evaporator blower is working.

Problem 3. The cooling blower is not operating. Compressors 1 and 2 and the condenser fan are operating.

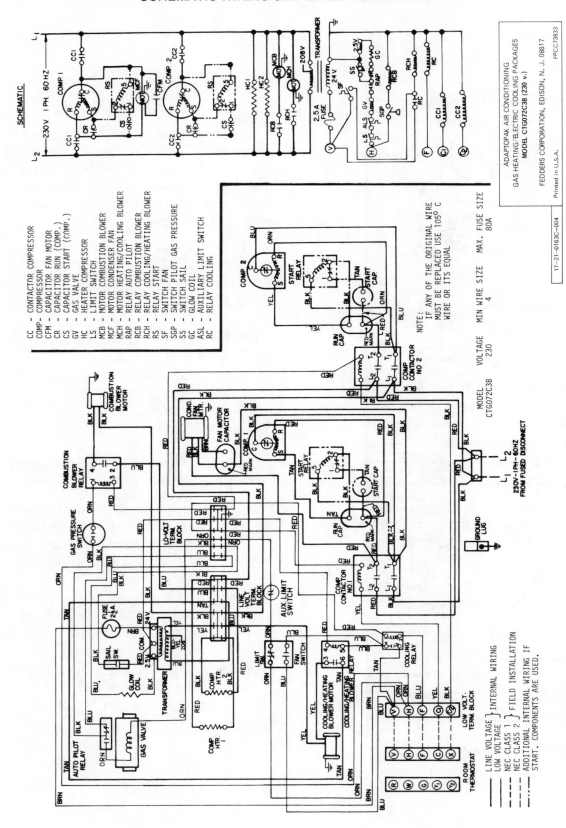

Having covered the cooling side of the schematic, now check the heating circuit. This heater is fired by natural gas. Due to high winds found on roof tops, a pilot flame could be extinguished easily. To solve this problem, a glow coil is used to automatically ignite the pilot whenever it is extinguished. Combustion air for the burners is supplied by the combustion blower which must operate before the gas valve will open.

A closer look at the wiring diagram will reveal that the transformer has a tapped secondary. This is a dual-voltage secondary with a common center tap. From the red common to the brown lead is 24 volts, and from the red common to the black lead is 2.5 volts. The 2.5 volts is used to energize the glow coil $\overset{}{\underset{GC}{\circ\!\!\wedge\!\!\wedge\!\!\wedge\!\!\circ}}$. A mistake in wiring at this point will cause the glow coil to burn out.

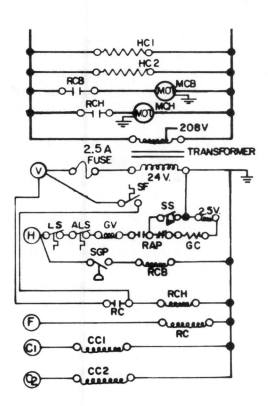

HEATING CYCLE

Place the thermostat on *heat*, fan on *auto*, and raise the thermostat setting to close the heating contacts. 230 volts is present at L_1 and L_2.

- With the thermostat closed and calling for heat, a circuit is completed from (V) to (H), energizing the combustion blower relay coil $\overset{}{\underset{RCB}{\circ\text{-}\text{mmm}\text{-}\circ}}$, if the gas pressure switch $\overset{SGP}{\underset{}{\circ\!\!\!\!\!\curlyvee\!\!\!\!\circ}}$ is closed. The gas pressure switch is connected to the main gas line and is closed if there is gas in the main line.

- Air velocity from the combustion blower will close the sail switch $\overset{SS}{\underset{}{\circ\!\!\!\text{-}\!\!\!\circ}}$, completing a circuit from the 2.5v transformer tap to the glow coil $\overset{}{\underset{GC}{\circ\!\!\wedge\!\!\wedge\!\!\circ}}$ through the normally closed half of the auto pilot relay $\overset{}{\underset{RAP}{\circ\text{-}\text{I}\!\circ\text{-}\!\#\!\circ}}$.

- The auto pilot relay has a set of normally-open and a set of normally-closed contacts. The pilot flame heats a thermocouple which opens the normally-closed contacts, breaking the circuit to the glow coil. Simultaneously, the normally-open contacts close, completing the 24v circuit to the gas valve coil $\overset{GV}{\underset{}{\circ\text{-}\text{mmm}\text{-}\circ}}$, through the normally-closed limit switch and the normally-closed auxiliary limit switch $\overset{ALS}{\underset{}{\circ\!\!\!\text{-}\!\!\!\circ}}$, when the sail switch $\overset{SS}{\underset{}{\circ\!\!\!\text{-}\!\!\!\circ}}$ is closed.

- Whenever the pilot flame goes out, the thermocouple cools, returning the auto pilot relay contacts $\overset{}{\underset{RAP}{\circ\text{-}\text{I}\!\circ\text{-}\!\#\!\circ}}$ to their normal position. The glow coil will not energize, again, unless the combustion blower motor is running, closing the sail switch. When the auto pilot relay is in the normal position, the gas valve $\overset{GV}{\underset{}{\circ\text{-}\text{mmm}\text{-}\circ}}$ is de-energized, shutting off the flow of gas to the burners.

- As the temperature in the heat exchanger rises to approximately 140°, the fan switch SF closes and, by bypassing contacts RC, completes a circuit from V to the cooling-heating blower motor relay coil RCH.

Recheck the low voltage circuit before tracing the high-voltage circuit.

- The energized coil RCB in the 24v circuit closes contacts RCB in the 230v circuit, starting the combustion blower motor MCB.

- With the blower motor relay coil RCH energized, contacts RCH in the 230v circuit close, starting the cooling-heating blower motor MCH.

Observe that if the heating contacts V to H in the thermostat open, the gas valve coil GV is de-energized, closing the flow of gas to the main burners.

Opening contacts V to H also breaks the circuit to the combustion blower relay coil RCB, opening contacts RCB, stopping the combustion motor MCB. As the combustion motor slows down, the sail switch SS opens, preventing the gas valve GV from opening and the glow coil GC from operating until the combustion motor is running.

The fan switch SF will not open, shutting off the blower motor MCH, until the temperature in the heat exchanger drops to approximately 120°.

Further observation will show that the combustion blower motor will continue to operate when either the limit switch LS or the auxiliary limit switch ALS is open, breaking the circuit to the gas valve coil.

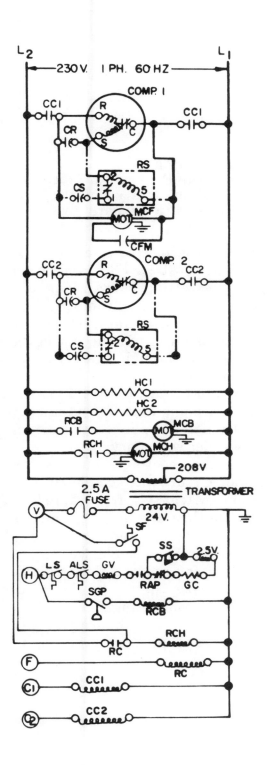

With the thermostat in the *heat* position, fan on *auto*, the thermostat contacts closed for heat, and the burners firing, what voltages would be read on a voltmeter across the following coils, switches and motors:

1. Coil RCB
2. Coil RCH
3. Coil GV
4. Coil GC
5. Switch SGP
6. Switch SS
7. Switch SF
8. Contacts RCB
9. Contacts RCH
10. Motor MCB
11. Motor MCH

Problem 1. Burner will not ignite. Pilot is on.

Problem 2. Heating-cooling blower motor will not run on heating, but will operate on cooling and constant fan position on thermostat.

Problem 3. The pilot is out and will not ignite automatically from glow coil.

WILLIAMSON
FIVE-IN-ONE OIL UNIT

The Williamson Five-in-One is a complete package consisting of an oil-fired, forced-air furnace, an air conditioning cooling coil for cooling and dehumidification, an electronic air cleaner for removing dust and other air-borne particles, and an automatic humidifier to add moisture to the air during the heating season.

The Five-in-One comes factory-wired, except for the low voltage control wire to the outside air conditioner condensing unit, low voltage humidistat, and low voltage thermostat. These parts are connected to the Five-in-One by field wiring.

The legend accompanying the wiring diagram is different from that used by other manufacturers. Williamson uses a solid line ——— for 115v, a dashed line with a dot —·—·— for 24v and a dashed line ——— for dc voltage. The dc voltage is developed in the electronic air cleaner power pack to supply the two cells with 4,000v dc and 8,000v dc.

The schematic shows all wires to be of equal weight and solid for 115v, 24v and field wiring.

The R856 or R8239 fan center is a Honeywell control, incorporating a 24v transformer ⫴R856/XFMR and a fan relay coil ◯FAN/RELAY, with a set of normally open contacts ⊥R856 to start the indoor fan motor ⒻAN/MTR.

The legend on the schematic indicates ◯ for terminals on the fan center, ☐ for thermostat subbase connections, and ◇ for terminals on the primary safety control.

1. GO STEP-BY-STEP
THROUGH THE ELECTRICAL SEQUENCE
To understand this schematic, we will cover each operation separately.

COOLING

Place the thermostat selector on COOL C┘O┘H•, fan on AUTO ⬝ON AUTO⬝ and lower the temperature setting below room temperature to close the cooling contacts COOL⊣⊢.

* With the cooling contacts closed, a circuit is completed from Ⓡ, one side of the 24v transformer, through ☐R☐ and the thermostat selector, to terminal Ⓨ, then to the compressor contactor coil ◯COOL/CONT, in the outside condensing unit. The circuit returns to terminal Ⓒ, the other side of the transformer secondary.

* When the cooling contacts closed, another circuit was completed, through the fan switch ⬝ON AUTO⬝, from ☐R☐ to ☐G☐. This energizes the fan relay ◯FAN/RELAY which is connected between Ⓖ and the return side of the transformer secondary Ⓒ.

* With the fan relay coil energized, the normally open contacts in the fan center close ⊥R856, completing a circuit from the 115v hot line, through terminal ③ to the fan motor ⒻAN/MTR and, from there, to the Ground wire.

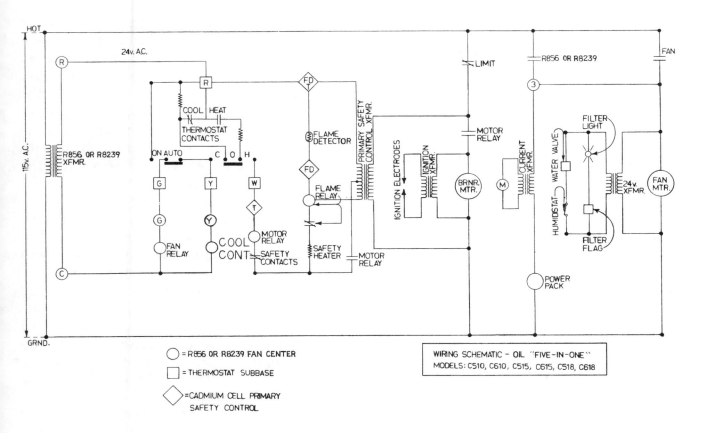

○ = R856 OR R8239 FAN CENTER

□ = THERMOSTAT SUBBASE

◇ = CADMIUM CELL PRIMARY SAFETY CONTROL

WIRING SCHEMATIC – OIL "FIVE-IN-ONE"
MODELS: C510, C610, C515, C615, C518, C618

HEATING CYCLE

Place the thermostat selector switch on HEAT, leave the fan switch on AUTO, and raise the temperature setting above room temperature to close the heating contacts.

The low voltage for the heating cycle is supplied by the primary safety control transformer, located in the oil primary control. The primary of the step-down transformer is wired between the HOT wire and Ground, through the normally closed contacts of the limit switch. The limit switch is set to open if the discharge air temperature exceeds 200°F. The opening of the limit switch will break the circuit to the transformer primary, shutting down the oil primary control.

- With the heating contacts closed, a circuit is completed from one side of the safety control transformer secondary, through FD and R, the thermostat and W, to terminal T on the primary control.

- From T, the circuit continues through the burner motor relay coil and the normally closed safety contacts, to the safety heater. From the safety heater, the circuit proceeds through the normally-closed flame relay contacts and the flame relay to the transformer secondary.

- With the burner motor relay coil energized, both sets of normally open motor relay contacts ⫟MOTOR RELAY close and the closed motor relay contacts in the 24v primary control complete a second circuit from the motor relay coil to the center tap ⫴PRIMARY CONTROL of the transformer secondary. The center tap supplies only a minimal voltage to keep the relay coil energized. The end tap of the transformer supplies a maximum voltage to energize the coil and pull in the relay.

- The second set of normally open motor relay contacts in the 115v circuit also closed, completing a circuit through the limit switch ⫟LIMIT to both the burner motor (BRNR MTR) and the primary of the 10,000v ignition transformer ⫴IGNITION XFMR. The motor starts and we get a spark at the ignition electrodes ⌐→ ←⌐. If the burner motor is pumping oil to the burner nozzle, we will get ignition.

- A flame detector ⊛FLAME DETECTOR is wired between terminals ⟨FP⟩ and ⟨FD⟩ and connected to the end tap of the primary transformer through the flame relay ⟨FLAME RELAY⟩. In the absence of light, the cad cell of the flame detector has a very high resistance and blocks the flow of current to the flame relay.

  However, when light from the oil flame strikes the flame detector, the resistance of the cad cell falls to a very low value and a circuit is completed, through the flame detector, to the flame relay.

- Energizing the flame relay opens the normally closed flame relay contacts ⫟⌐ and takes the safety heater ⫴SAFETY HEATER out of the circuit, thereby assuring that the safety contacts ⫟SAFETY CONTACTS will not open.

Had the oil failed to ignite, the flame detector would have blocked the current flow to the flame relay and, after 45 seconds, the safety heater would have opened the safety contacts and cut off the entire oil delivery and ignition systems by deactivating the motor relay. The oil burner cannot be restarted, even with the thermostat calling for heat, until the safety heater has cooled and the safety contacts closed.

On restart, only 45 seconds are allowed for ignition. If ignition is not achieved in these few seconds, the safety heater will once again open the safety contacts.

- The normally open fan contacts ⫟FAN are set to close when the temperature in the heat exchanger reaches 110°F and have a cutout temperature differential of approximately 25°. The closed fan contacts complete the circuit to the fan motor from HOT to Ground.

  The fan motor is not controlled by the low voltage control circuit and will continue to run until the temperature in the heat exchanger drops to the cutout temperature, even though the primary control or limit switch has shut down the system on safety. Thus, the fan continues to operate as long as the air it delivers is at a comfortable temperature.

- A 115v to 24v step-down transformer ⫴24v XFMR is wired parallel to the fan motor (FAN MTR) and is hot whenever the fan motor is energized. Wired across the 24v secondary is a filter flag switch ⊓↖. The filter flag switch is a normally open switch that is kept open by the flow of air through the filter. When the filter becomes blocked, restricting the air flow, the flag switch will close and energize the filter light ⊗ which warns that the filter needs to be replaced.

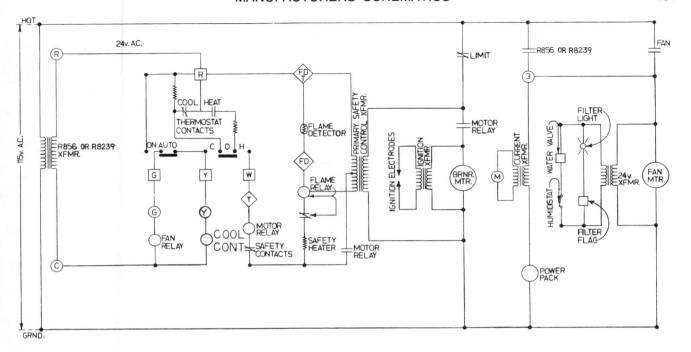

HUMIDIFIER

The humidifier adds moisture to the return air when the humidistat closes ᴴᵁᴹᴵᴰᴵˢᵀᴬᵀ⁀. To prevent the humidifier from operating when the fan is off, the 24v control transformer ⫘ₓꜰₘᵣ is wired parallel to fan motor. The water valve ⁻ʷᴬᵀᴱᴿ ⱽᴬᴸⱽᴱ⁀ in the humidifier is opened by a 24v solenoid coil wired in series with the humidistat.

ELECTRONIC AIR CLEANER

The electronic air cleaner will remove and hold airborne particles and should only operate when the fan motor is running.

To make sure that air cleaner operates only when the motor is running, the power pack ○ᴾᴼᵂᴱᴿ ᴾᴬᶜᴷ (which is the complete control circuit for the air cleaner) and the current transformer ⫘ᶜᵁᴿᴿᴱᴺᵀ ₓꜰₘᵣ (that controls the operation of the performance meter Ⓜ mounted on the air cleaner door) are wired in series with the fan center contacts ⊣ᴿ⁸⁵⁶ (cooling) and the temperature operated contacts of the fan relay ⊥ꜰᴬᴺ (heating). The closing of either set of contacts will energize the electronic air cleaner through terminal ③.

Set the thermostat to HEAT, fan to AUTO and raise the temperature setting of the thermostat to close Ⓡ to Ⓦ. Let the fan start.

Now, what voltages would you read across the following coils, switches and motors:

1. Motor relay coil ○ᴹᴼᵀᴼᴿ ᴿᴱᴸᴬʸ
2. Flame relay coil ⊢ꜰᴸᴬᴹᴱ ᴿᴱᴸᴬʸ⊣
3. Fan motor Ⓕᴬᴺ ᴹᵀᴿ
4. Burner motor Ⓑᴿᴺᴿ ᴹᵀᴿ
5. Fan switch ⊥ꜰᴬᴺ
6. Motor relay contacts ⊣ᴹᴼᵀᴼᴿ ᴿᴱᴸᴬʸ
7. Flame relay contacts ⊬⊢⌐
8. Filter flag ⊓⤙
9. Humidistat (open) ᴴᵁᴹᴵᴰᴵˢᵀᴬᵀ⁀

Solve these problems using the five-step procedure:

Problem 1. Fan motor will not run in the cooling cycle.

Problem 2. Burner motor and ignition cut out after 45 seconds.

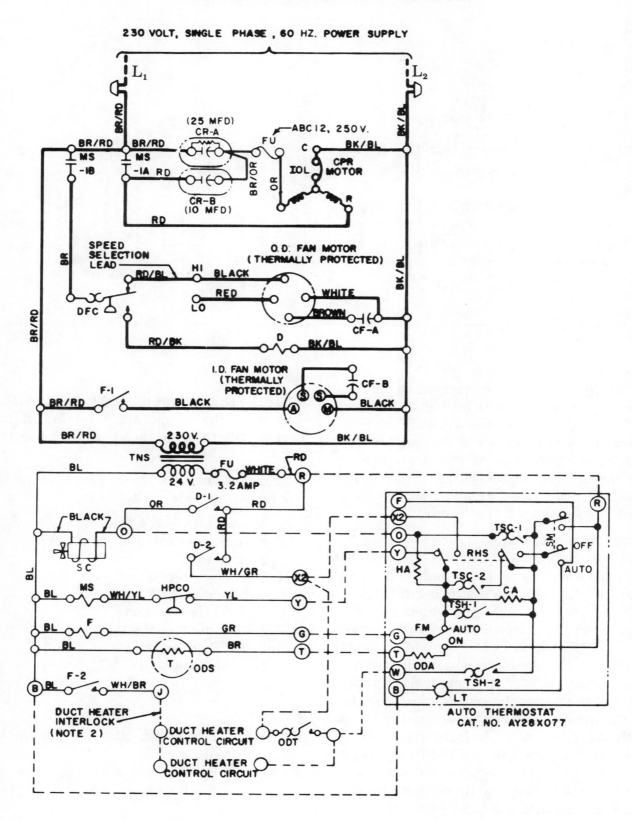

GENERAL ELECTRIC
SINGLE PACKAGE HEAT PUMP

The heat pump is basically an air conditioner that will cool in summer and heat in winter.

To better understand the operation of the heat pump, imagine it first as an ordinary window air conditioner. The inside coil, or evaporator, extracts heat from the room and expels it, through the outside coil, or condenser, to the outside air.

Now imagine that, in the fall, the window air conditioner is reversed, with the condenser being the inside coil and the evaporator being the outside coil. Your air conditioner will now extract heat from the outside air and expel it into the room.

The heat pump reverses the operation of the air conditioner very simply, by means of a four-way reversing valve. When the valve is shifted, by a change in temperature, the flow of refrigerant is reversed. This, in effect, converts the evaporator into a condenser and the condenser into the evaporator. The automatic operation of this reversing valve is controlled by a wall-mounted thermostat that signals whether heating or cooling is required in the conditioned space.

1. GO STEP-BY-STEP
THROUGH THE ELECTRICAL SEQUENCE.

COOLING CYCLE

A 24v thermostat is used for heat pump operation. There are two stages of heat, TSH-1 and TSH-2 $\overset{\text{TSH-2}}{\cancel{\times}}$, and two stages of cooling TSC-1 and TSC-2 $\overset{\text{TSC-2}}{\cancel{\times}}$.

This model thermostat has an AUTO position on the selector switch. The system will automatically switch from cooling to heating or heating to cooling as the temperature at the thermostat changes.

Set the thermostat switch on AUTO, fan on AUTO and lower the thermostat setting to close the first stage cooling contacts only. 230 volts is present at L_1 and L_2.

- With the thermostat contacts $\overset{\text{TSC-1}}{\cancel{\times}}$ closed and the system switch on AUTO, a circuit is completed from the fused side of the 24v transformer, through ⓡ ⓡ, to the ⓞ terminal on the thermostat subbase.

- From ⓞ, field wiring ——— is connected to the ⓞ terminal on the outside unit. The circuit from ⓞ energizes the solenoid coil on the reversing or switchover valve, changing the valve's position to cooling. The circuit is completed to the other side of the transformer secondary.

- Should the temperature around the thermostat rise another 1½°, the second stage cooling contacts $\overset{\text{TSC-2}}{\cancel{\times}}$ close, making a circuit to ⓨ on the subbase.

- From ⓨ, field wiring ——— is connected to ⓨ in the outside unit. The circuit from ⓨ energizes the compressor motor contactor coil through the high pressure cut-out, completing the circuit back to the other side of the transformer.

- When the second stage contact in the thermostat closed, a circuit was also initiated to terminal Ⓖ on the subbase, through the fan switch ⟋⟋ which was set in the AUTO position.
- From Ⓖ on the subbase, field wiring is connected to terminal Ⓖ in the outside unit, energizing the indoor fan relay coil ⟋⟋, completing the circuit back to the transformer.

At this point, note that the first stage of cooling TSC-1 only energizes the switchover valve solenoid ⟋⟋. This indicates that the switchover valve is normally in the heating position. If the switchover valve solenoid failed while in the cooling cycle, the switchover valve would change back to the heating position. Note, too, that the second stage in the thermostat is the only control for the compressor motor contactor coil and the indoor fan relay coil.

Now, trace the high voltage cooling circuit.

- With the main disconnect in the *on* position, 230 volts is supplied to the high side of the step-down control transformer ⟋⟋.
- A trickle circuit is hot from the line side of the compressor motor contactor ⟋⟋, through the resistor ⟋⟋ in the run capacitor and the fuse ⟋⟋ to the start terminal on the compressor ⟋⟋. This trickle circuit provides approximately 40 watts of continous heat. The circuit continues through the internal overload protector ϑ to the common terminal C on the compressor. The circuit is completed from C to Line L_2.

- With the compressor motor contactor coil ⟋⟋ in the 24v circuit energized, the normally open contacts ⟋⟋ and ⟋⟋ close.
- With contacts ⟋⟋ closed, a circuit is completed through the run terminal ⟋⟋ of the compressor to the common c o terminating at L_2. Another circuit is completed, through the run capacitor ⟋⟋ and the fuse ⟋⟋, to the start winding of this PSC motor. The circuit continues through the internal protector ϑ to the common terminal C and L_2.
- The other set of contacts ⟋⟋ in the compressor motor contactor are also closed. This completes a circuit through the defrost control ⟋⟋, which is used to defrost the outside coil during the heating cycle. From the defrost control, the circuit continues to the high speed terminal ⟋⟋ of the outdoor fan motor. The outdoor fan motor is a two-speed permanent split capacitor (PSC) ⟋⟋ motor. The circuit is completed from the motor to L_2.
- When TSC-2 in the thermostat closed, the indoor fan relay coil ⟋⟋ was energized, closing the normally open contacts ⟋⟋ in the 230v circuit.
- With the contacts of the indoor fan motor relay closed, a circuit is completed to the indoor fan motor and L_2. The schematic shows the indoor fan motor to be a permanent split capacitor ⟋⟋ type.

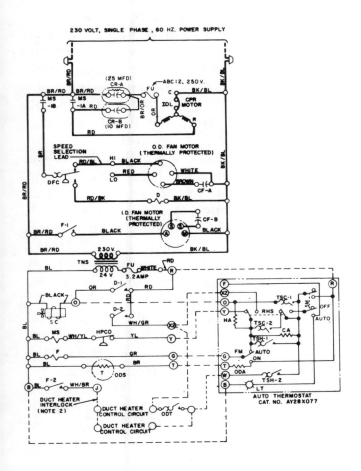

Note that the compressor motor contactor controls the compressor with one set of contacts and the outdoor fan motor (O.D.) with another set of contacts. When the compressor motor contactor contacts are open, trickle voltage is still present at the start and common terminals of the compressor. Unlike previous examples, these contacts only break the L_1 line to the compressor and the outdoor fan motor, rather than both L_1 and L_2.

With the cooling side of the schematic completed, set the thermostat selector switch to AUTO and the fan switch on AUTO. Lower the thermostat setting to close both stages of cooling.

What voltages would be read, on a voltmeter, across the following:

1. Coil
2. Coil
3. Coil
4. Switch
5. Switch
6. Switch
7. I.D. Fan Motor A to M
8. CPR Motor C to R
9. O.D. Fan Motor HI to WHITE

Using the five-step procedure, solve these three problems:

Problem 1. Hot air coming out of supply ducts in the summer. The compressor and outdoor and indoor fans are operating.

Problem 2. The compressor and outdoor fan are not operating. The indoor fan is operating.

Problem 3. The outdoor fan is not running. The compressor and indoor fan are both operating with the compressor cycling on the high pressure cutout.

HEATING CYCLE

To check the heating cycle, place the system selector switch on **AUTO**, the fan switch on **AUTO** and move the control arm to close the contacts to the first stage of heat.

- With the thermostat contacts ^{TSH-1} closed, a circuit is run from Ⓡ to Ⓡ through the selector switch and the contacts to Ⓨ on the subbase.

- Ⓨ, on the subbase, is field connected ——— to the Ⓨ terminal on the heat pump. From Ⓨ, the circuit continues through the high pressure cutout ^{HPCO} to the compressor motor contactor coil ^{MS} and terminates at the transformer. With the coil energized, contacts ^{MS}_{1-1A} and ^{MS}_{1-1B}, in the 230v circuit, close, starting the compressor and the outdoor fan motor.

- When the first stage heating contacts closed, another circuit was completed through the heat anticipator HA to Ⓞ. Although Ⓞ is field wired ——— to terminal Ⓞ on the heat pump, the switch-over valve coil is not energized due to the high resistance of the heat anticipator. Voltage drop, through the resistor, prevents the valve from shifting out of the heating position.

- Closing of the first stage heating contacts ^{TSH-1} energizes a third circuit, through the indoor fan relay coil ^F. The energized indoor fan relay coil closes contacts ^{F-1} starting the indoor fan motor.

At this point, the heating system is operating on the compressor only. However, as outside temperatures drop, the heat pump may not be able to extract enough heat from the outside air. To supplement the heat output of the pump, electric resistance heaters are installed in the supply duct, and are controlled by the second stage of heat ^{TSH-2} in the thermostat.

- If the temperature at the thermostat drops 1½° below the thermostat setting, contacts ^{TSH-2} close and complete a circuit from Ⓡ, through the selector switch, to Ⓦ on the subbase. Field wiring connects Ⓦ to the normally open outdoor temperature switch ^{ODT} and completes a circuit, through the first of two duct heater control circuits, to Ⓙ.

- When the indoor fan relay coil ^F was energized, it closed contacts ^{F-1}, starting the fan motor, and contacts ^{F-2}, completing the circuit from the first duct heater control circuit to Ⓑ and the return side of the transformer. Having the two switches, F-1 and F-2, in tandem assures that the fan is operating while the resistance heaters are energized. (Because the heaters themselves are accessories, they are not shown in this schematic.)

- The outdoor thermostat is set to close at an outdoor temperature where additional electric resistance heat will be required. This temperature setting is related to the heat loss of the structure and the capacity of the resistance heating units. When the outdoor thermostat closes, the circuit to the second duct heater control circuit is completed, through Ⓙ and ^{F-2} to Ⓑ.

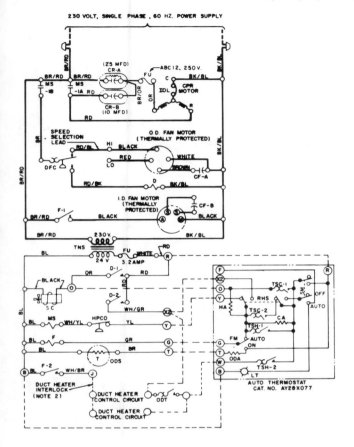

- From ⊗2 on the subbase, field wiring —— is connected to ⊗2 in the outside unit. Another field wire is run to the duct heater control circuit, bypassing the outdoor thermostat ⌇ODT, and energizing the second duct heater regardless of the outdoor temperature.
- If the temperature around the thermostat drops 1½° below the thermostat setting, heating contacts ⌇TSH-2 will close, energizing the first duct heater.
- Heating contacts ⌇TSH-1 will already be closed to keep the indoor fan motor running by energizing the coil ⌇F. The indoor fan motor will continue to run until the first stage of heat is satisfied.
- When the emergency heat switch was shifted to *on*, a light ⌇LT on the thermostat came on through a circuit from Ⓑ on the subbase to Ⓑ in the outside unit, being completed through the *on* contacts of the emergency heat switch and the AUTO contacts of the thermostat switch.

- In the event of a failure in the heat pump, emergency heat may be required until the heat pump can be repaired. At this time, the emergency heat switch ⌇RHS in the thermostat is manually shifted to the *on* position.
- With the emergency heat switch in the *on* position, the circuits from Ⓡ, through heating contacts ⌇TSH-1 to Ⓨ are opened, de-energizing the compressor motor contactor coil ⌇MS, shutting off the compressor motor and outdoor fan motor by opening contacts ⌇MS-1A and ⌇MS-1B in the 230v circuit.
- When the emergency heat switch is in the *on* position, a circuit is run from Ⓡ through heating contacts ⌇TSH-1 to terminal ⊗2 on the subbase.

Observing the heating cycle, we can determine:
- The normal position of the switchover valve is in the heating position.
- A resistance-free circuit must be made from Ⓡ to Ⓞ to reverse the switchover valve position for cooling.
- The indoor fan relay coil must be energized, closing contact F-2 from Ⓙ to Ⓑ before the duct heaters will energize.
- The emergency resistance heat switch will de-energize the refrigerant system and energize the supplementary resistance heater circuit.
- If the high pressure cutout ⌇HPCO opens, both the compressor and the outdoor fan will stop and the other systems will remain operative.

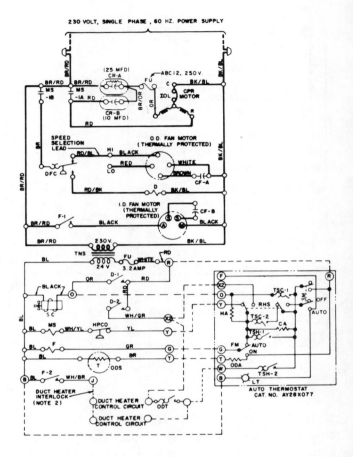

DEFROST CYCLE

Periodically, during the heating cycle, the outdoor coil will require defrosting. This is accomplished automatically whenever the thermostatic bellows in the defrost control senses below-freezing temperatures and the pressure sensor in the defrost control indicates that air flow through the coil is blocked by ice. The system is in the heating cycle with contacts TSH-1 closed.

- When icing occurs, the defrost control which is a single-pole, double-throw switch, breaks the circuit to the outdoor fan motor (O.D.), stopping the outdoor fan.

- At the same time, the defrost control completes a circuit to energize the defrost relay coil in the 230v circuit.

- With defrost relay coil energized, contacts D-1 and D-2, in the 24v circuit, close.

- When closed, contact D-1 completes a circuit from (R) to (O), energizing the switchover valve solenoid and changing the switchover valve to the cooling position, bypassing the thermostat.

- When closed, contact D-2 completes a circuit from (R) on the transformer to (X2) and then to the duct heater control, bypassing the thermostat.

- The energized electric resistance heater is used to temper or warm the cool air now coming from the indoor coil.

- As the ice on the outdoor coil melts, the static pressure difference is reduced and the outdoor coil temperature reaches between 50 to 60 °F, the defrost control will change position, restarting the outdoor fan, de-energizing the defrost relay coil, opening contacts D-1 and D-2.

- With defrost relay contacts D-1 and D-2 open, the switchover valve solenoid is de-energized, returning the switchover valve to the heating position, and opening the circuit to the duct heater.

THE ANTICIPATOR CIRCUITS

The function of the heating anticipator and the cooling anticipator was covered in Section II along with the thermostat. Note that the cooling anticipator ᴄᴬ is energized whenever the system switch or thermostat is on AUTO. The heating anticipator ʜᴬ is energized when the thermostat is on AUTO and the first stage heating ᵀˢʜ⁻¹ switch is closed.

A third anticipator circuit ᴼᴰᴬ is energized whenever line voltage is available, even with the thermostat off. Its purpose is to furnish a variable amount of heat, depending on the outdoor temperature.

The outdoor anticipator ᴼᴰᴬ, located in the thermostat, is connected in series with an outdoor sensor ᴼᴰˢ, actually a thermistor, that is exposed to the outdoor air. The thermistor has the ability to vary its resistance with rises and falls in temperature. In this case, the resistance of the thermistor increases with a temperature drop.

With colder outdoor temperatures, more resistance heat is generated at the thermistor than at the thermostat heat anticipator. Thus, the thermostat senses less *false heat* and the heating system runs longer on each cycle.

At warmer outdoor temperatures, the thermistor has less resistance and the thermostat anticipator generates more heat, thereby fooling the thermostat and foreshortening the heating system running time on each cycle.

With the heating and defrosting schematic completed, set the thermostat selector switch to AUTO, the fan to AUTO and raise the thermostat to close the first stage of heat.

What voltages would you read across the following:

1. Coil ᴹˢ
2. Coil ᴼᶠ
3. Coil ᶜ
4. Contact DFC to HI
5. Contacts ᶠ⁻¹
6. Contacts ᶠ⁻²
7. Contacts (TSH-1A)
8. Contacts (TSH-1B)

Using the five-step procedure, solve these three problems:

Problem 1. Compressor is not running. Outdoor and indoor fans are running.

Problem 2. Indoor fan, compressor and outdoor fan are not running.

Problem 3. One duct heater will not energize. Second stage contacts TSH-2 are closed. Compressor, outdoor fan and indoor fan are all operating.

Section VI

TROUBLESHOOTING SOLUTIONS

APRILAIRE

1. Furnace blower motor ○ BLOWER MOTOR   **115v**
2. Humidifier fan motor ⊙   **115v**
3. Water valve solenoid coil   **115v**
4. Electromagnetic relay coil   **24v**
5. Secondary of transformer   **24v**
6. Humidistat contacts   **0v**
7. Relay contacts   **0v**

Problem 2.

STEP 1. Has been completed.

STEPS 2 and 3. Blower motor is running, voltage and fuses are alright.

STEP 4. Water valve and fan motor will not operate.

STEP 5.

☐ Check the transformer secondary. If you do not read 24v, the transformer is defective.

☐ Check the relay coil. If 24v is read, the relay is defective.

☐ Check the relay contacts. If 115v is read, the relay is defective.

☐ Check the humidistat. If 24v is read, the humidistat is defective.

☐ Check the water valve and the fan motor, although it is unlikely that they would fail together. If you read 115v, the units are defective.

FRIGIDAIRE

COOL

1. Freezer mullion drier, Line 1   **115v**
2. Door drier, Line 6   **115v**
3. Center vertical drier, Line 7   **115v**
4. Defrost heaters, Line 7   **115v**
5. Cold control heater, Line 8   **115v**
6. Freezer fan, Line 9   **115v**
7. Condenser fan, Line 11   **115v**
8. Defrost timer motor, terminals 1 to 3, Line 13   **115v**
9. Common to run on the compressor, Line 13   **115v**
10. Cold control, Line 9   **0v**
11. Motor protector, Line 10   **0v**

DEFROST

1. Freezer mullion drier, Line 1   **115v**
2. Door drier, Line 6   **115v**
3. Center vertical drier, Line 7   **0v**
4. Defrost heaters, Line 7   **115v**
5. Cold control heater, Line 8   **0v**
6. Freezer fan, Line 9   **0v**
7. Condenser fan, Line 11   **0v**
8. Defrost timer motor, terminals 1 to 3, Line 13   **115v**
9. Common to run on the compressor, Line 13   **0v**
10. Cold control, Line 9   **0v**
11. Motor protector, Line 10   **0v**

Problem 1.

STEP 1. Has been covered.

STEPS 2 and 3. Since the box cools, the voltage and fuses are alright.

STEP 4. Refrigerator will not defrost.

STEP 5.

☐ Check the voltage across the defrost heater. If voltage is read, and the box needs defrosting, the heater coil is defective.

☐ Check the defrost thermostat. If voltage is read, the thermostat is open.

☐ Check for 115v between terminals 3 and 4 of the defrost timer. If voltage is read, the timer motor is defective.

If no voltage is read, there is a broken wire between terminal 3 and B or between terminal 1 and W.

Problem 2.

STEP 1. Has been completed.

STEPS 2 and 3. Partial operation indicates that the voltage and fuses are good.

STEP 4. Refrigerator will not cease defrosting.

STEP 5.

☐ Check between terminals 3 and 4 of the defrost timer. If no voltage is read, the switch is closed.

If voltage is read, the system should not be in defrost.

☐ Check the timer motor between terminals 1 and 3. If voltage is read, the motor is defective.

If no voltage is read, there is a broken wire . . . usually from terminal 1 to W.

Problem 3.

STEP 1. Has been completed.

STEPS 2 and 3. The fans are working, the voltage and fuses must be good.

STEP 4. Compressor will not start. There is no hum.

STEP 5.

The schematic shows that the compressor and both fans are switched on by the cold control.

☐ Check for voltage from the compressor common terminal to W. If voltage is read, there is a broken wire between these two points.

☐ Check the motor protector. If voltage is read, the protector is open.

If no voltage is read, wait for the internal overload to reset.

☐ Check the compressor relay between terminals 2 and 4. If voltage is read, the relay is defective. Otherwise, there is a broken wire between the compressor and its relay.

HEIL

1. Ⓡ to Ⓒ on the compressor   **230v**
2. RUN to common on the
   condenser fan motor   **230v**
3. Ⓛ to Ⓣ on the contactor   **0v**
4. Ⓡ to Ⓨ on the thermostat   **0v**
5. Ⓡ to Ⓨ on the condensing
   unit contactor coil   **24v**
6. Primary of transformer   **115v**

Problem 1.

STEP 1. Has been completed.

STEPS 2 and 3. Compressor is running, voltage and fuses are alright.

STEP 4. Condenser fan is not running.

STEP 5.

☐ Check terminals RUN to common on the condenser motor. If voltage is read, the internal protector is open or the run capacitor is defective or the motor is defective.

☐ Check the solid state, variable speed FAN CONTROL by checking for voltage between the common terminal of the fan motor and terminal T of the contactor. If you read 230v, the speed controller is open or there is a broken wire between the two points.

☐ Check the wiring from RUN on the condenser motor to the other terminal T on the contactor. If you read 230v the wire between the two points is broken.

Problem 2.

STEP 1. Has been completed.

STEPS 2 and 3. The wiring diagram shows that there are two field-wired power supplies: 115v for the fan, 230v for the compressor and condenser motors. Therefore, check the voltage and fuses for the 230v supply.

STEP 4. The compressor and condenser motors are not running. Since the blower motor is operating, we know that there is 24v available to both the fan center and the condensing unit contactor coil.

STEP 5.

☐ Check for voltage between terminals R and C on both the compressor and condenser motors. The odds are against finding both motors defective at the same time, but a 230v reading will prove that that is the case.

☐ Check for voltage between both sets of terminals L and T on the motor contactor.

If you read 230v across one set of contacts, the contactor is defective. If you read 230v over both sets of contacts, the contactor is open.

☐ Check the condensing unit contactor coil in the 24v circuit. If you read 24v, the coil is defective.

☐ Check for voltage between R and Y on the thermostat. If 24v is read, the thermostat is defective.

☐ Check the wiring from Y on the thermostat to Y on the contactor coil. If 24v is read, the wire in broken.

Problem 3.

STEP 1. Has been completed.

STEPS 2 and 3. Check the voltage and fuses for both the 115v and 230v supplies, since none of the motors are running.

STEP 4. All the motors are inoperative.

STEP 5.

☐ Check the 24v transformer first, since it supplies the control circuit. If you read 115v across the primary and no voltage across the 24v secondary, the transformer is defective.

☐ Check across terminals R to Y and R to G in the thermostat. If you read 24v, the thermostat is defective.

☐ Check from terminal R on the thermostat to the transformer. If you read 24v, there is a broken wire between the two points.

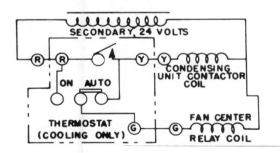

Revised thermostat schematic. *Courtesy Heil-Quaker.*

SCOTSMAN

1. Master switch	**0v**
2. Bin thermostat	**0v**
3. Low pressure control	**0v**
4. Spout switch	**0v**
5. Fan control (motor at low speed)	**220v**
6. Fan motor (motor at high speed)	**220v**
7. Auger motor	**220v**
8. Contactor coil	**220v**

Problem 1.

STEP 1. Has been completed.

STEPS 2 and 3. The compressor is running, so there is no need to check voltage and fuses.

STEP 4. Fan motor is not running.

STEP 5.

☐ If there is 220v at the fan motor terminals, the fan is defective.

☐ Check the fan resistor. If 220v is read, the resistor is open.

☐ If there is no voltage at any of these points, look for a broken wire.

Problem 2.

STEP 1. Has been completed.

STEPS 2 and 3. Check the voltage and fuses. This is a 3-phase compressor. If the L_2 phase is out, the auger motor can still operate.

STEP 4. The compressor and condenser fan motor are inoperative.

STEP 5.

☐ Check the 3-phase contactor. If voltage is read across any of the contacts, L_1 to T_1, L_2 to T_2, L_3 to T_3, the contacts are defective.

If there is no voltage at any of the contacts, the contacts are open. With the contacts open, voltage can be read from L_1 to L_2 to L_3, but not from L_1 to T_1, etc.

☐ Check the contactor coil. If voltage is read, the coil is defective.

☐ Check the spout switch. If voltage is read, the switch is open.

☐ Check the voltage at the normally closed overload at the auger drive.

If no voltage is present, there is a broken wire between the overload switch and the contactor coil.

Problem 3.

STEP 1. Has been completed.

STEPS 2 and 3. If nothing is running, first check the voltage and fuses on all three lines.

STEP 4. Nothing is operating.

STEP 5.

☐ The schematic shows three switches in series, each one of which could render the system inoperative. They are the master switch, the bin thermostat, and the low pressure control. Check each of these switches. If voltage is read, the switch is open.

☐ If two or more switches are open, voltage can only be read from L_1 on the contactor to the auger motor terminal.

ARKLA

1. Relay contacts   0v
2. Time delay contacts   0v
3. Sail switch   0v
4. Chilled water switch   0v
5. Hi-temperature switch   0v
6. Gas valve coil   24v
7. Time delay relay coil   24v
8. Relay coil   24v
9. Pump motor   230v
10. Run to common on fan motor   230v

Problem 1.

STEP 1. Has been completed.
STEP 2. Check for 24v at the transformer secondary.
STEP 3. If there is no 24v, check the fuses to the transformer primary.
STEP 4. The gas valve will not open.
STEP 5.

☐ The gas valve has a 24v solenoid coil. Check the coil. If 24v is present, the coil is defective.

If there is no voltage, check the mechanical linkage within the valve body. It may be defective although the coil is good.

☐ Both the sail switch and the chilled water switch are in series with the gas valve. If 24v is read across either switch, that switch is open.

If the sail switch is open, the fan motor is not running.

If the chilled water switch is open, it should close if the water temperature is 42°.

☐ Check the thermostat. If 24v is read across terminals R to Y, the thermosat is defective.

☐ Check the high temp switch. If 24v is present, the switch is open.

If no voltage is available, a wire is broken.

Problem 2.

STEP 1. Has been completed.
STEP 2. Check for 230v between L_1 and L_2.
STEP 3. If there is no voltage, check the fuses.
STEP 4. Fan and pump motor will not start.
STEP 5.

☐ Check the voltage at the terminals of each motor. If 230v is read at each motor, they are both defective.

If 230v is read at only one motor, check for a broken wire.

☐ Check the relay contacts. If there is no voltage, a wire is broken.

If 230v is read, the contacts are open.

☐ Check the relay coil in the 24v circuit. If 24v is read across the relay coil, the coil is defective.

☐ Check the time delay switch. If there is no voltage, look for a broken wire to the transformer secondary.

If 24v is read, the contacts are open.

☐ Check voltage to the relay heater. If 24v is read, wait approximately one minute for the contacts to close. If they do not close, the TD relay is defective.

☐ Check the thermostat. If 24v is read across R to Y, the thermostat is defective.

☐ Check the high temp switch. If 24v is read, the switch is open.

If there is no voltage, a wire is broken.

YORK

COOLING

1. Coil ⌇⌇⌇ CCH (Line 2)	**230v**
2. Coil Ⓜ (Line 14)	**24v**
3. Coil ⑥Ⓡ (Line 13)	**24v**
4. Contacts ┤├ M (Lines 3, 4, 7)	**0v**
5. Contacts ⊁ HPC (Line 14)	**0v**
6. Contacts ⊥10L, ⊁20L, ⊁30L (Line 14)	**0v**
7. Contacts ┤├ 6R (Line 9)	**0v**
8. Compressor Terminals 1 to 2, 2 to 3, 1 to 3	**230v**
9. Condenser Fan Motor Terminals T1 to T2	**230v**
10. Blower Motor Terminals	**230v**

Problem 1.

STEP 1. Has been completed.

STEPS 2 and 3. Compressor is running, voltage and fuses are alright.

STEP 4. Blower motor is not running.

STEP 5.

☐ Check the voltage at the blower motor terminals. If 230v is read, the motor is defective.

☐ Check the 6R relay contacts. If 230v is read, the contacts are open.

If no voltage is available at the relay, there is a broken wire between L1 and L3.

☐ Check coil 6R in the 24v circuit. If 24v is read, the coil is defective.

☐ Check the thermostat. If 24v is read from V to F, the thermostat is defective.

If no voltage is available at the thermostat, the wire from terminal F on the thermostat to terminal F on the package unit is broken.

Problem 2.

STEP 1. Has been completed.

STEPS 2 and 3. The blower motor will operate if fuse L2 is open. The compressor and the condenser will not. Check voltage and fuses.

STEP 4. Compressor and condenser fan are not running.

STEP 5.

☐ Check the compressor and condenser fan motor terminals, even though it is improbable that both both motors are simultaneously defective. However, if you read 230v, the motor is defective or the internal overloads are open.

☐ Check from the load side of contact M on Line 3 to the load side of contacts M on Lines 4 and 7.

If 230v is read, the contacts are closed and one or more wires on the load side of the contacts is broken.

If no voltage is read, the contacts are open.

☐ Check coil M in the 24v circuit. If 24v is read, the coil is defective.

☐ Check the safety switches: 1OL, 2OL, 3OL, HPC. If 24v is read across any switch, that switch is open.

☐ Check from terminal C to terminal T on Line 14. If 24v is read, there is more than one safety switch open.

☐ Check the thermostat. If 24v is read from terminals V to C, the thermostat is defective.

If no voltage is present, the wire from C in the thermostat to C in the air conditioner is broken.

HEATING

1. The HR coils (Lines 25A, 25, 24, 23, 22, 21) — **20v dc**
2. Coil ③R (Line 19) — **20v dc**
3. Heater element ⌁⌁3H⌁⌁ (Line 26) **230v ac**
4. Heater element ⌁⌁5H⌁⌁ (Line 28) **230v ac**
5. Contacts ≠2TLS (Line 17) — **0v**
6. Contacts ≠1TLS (Line 18) — **0v**
7. Contacts ⊣⊢2HR (Line 26) — **0v**
8. Contacts ⊣⊢6HR (Line 28) — **0v**
9. Contacts ⊣⊢3HR (Line 8) — **0v**
10. Blower Motor Terminals (Lines 8, 9) — **230v ac**

Problem 3.

STEP 1. Has been completed.

STEPS 2 and 3. If the condenser fan and the blower motor are running, all three fuses are good.

STEP 4. Compressor is not running.

STEP 5.

□ Check for voltage at the compressor terminals. If 230v is read, the compressor is defective.

□ Check from T1 to T3. If no voltage is read, contacts M on Line 7 are open and the contactor is defective, even though the other two contacts M are supplying power to the condenser fan.

If voltage is read, there is a broken wire.

□ The overloads are apparently closed. If one them was open, the condenser fan would not be operating.

Problem 1.

STEP 1. Has been completed.

STEPS 2 and 3. Each bank of heaters is separately fused. The fuses must be checked.

STEP 4. Elements 4H, 5H, and 6H do not heat.

STEP 5.

□ Check each heater. If 230v is read, the heater is defective.

□ Check fuses 4FL, 5FL, 6FL. If 230v is read, the fuse is open.

□ Check contacts 4HR, 5HR, 6HR. If 230v is read, the contacts are open.

□ Check relay coil 4HR on Line 23. If 20v dc is read, the coil is defective. (Relays 5HR and 6HR need not be checked since they will not energize until 4HR is energized.)

□ Check the time delay relay 3TR on Line 18. This relay must be energized to close a circuit to relay 4HR. If 20v dc is read, the relay is defective.

If no voltage is available, a wire to the coil is open.

Problem 2.

STEP 1. Has been completed.

STEPS 2 and 3. Check the fuses. If L2 is open, heater 1H will still operate.

STEP 4. Elements 2H and 3H will not operate.

STEP 5.

☐ Check heaters 2H and 3H. If 230v is read, the heaters are defective.

☐ Check fusible links 2FL and 3FL. If 230v is read, the fuses are open.

☐ If no voltage is available to the heaters, a wire is open from L2.

☐ Check the 1TR relay. If 20v dc is read, the relay is defective.

☐ Check the 2HR relay. If 20v dc is read, the relay is defective.

☐ The suceeding relays should be alright, since they sequence from those that preceed.

Problem 3.

STEP 1. Has been completed.

STEPS 2 and 3. Check voltage and fuses. The blower is not in the heater circuit.

STEP 4. Blower motor is not running.

STEP 5.

☐ Check the blower motor. If 230v ac is read, the blower is defective.

☐ Check the 3R contacts, Line 8. If 230v is read, the contacts are open.

If no voltage is available, a field wire is open.

☐ Check the 3R relay coil, Line 19. If 20v dc is read, the coil is defective.

☐ Check from terminal F to F2, Line 19. If voltage is read, a wire is open to coil 3R.

If no voltage is available, a wire is open inside the sequencer.

FEDDERS

COOLING

1. Coil	$CC1$	24v
2. Coil	$CC2$	24v
3. Coil	RC	24v
4. Coil	RCH	24v
5. Coil	$HC1$	230v
6. Contacts	RC	0v
7. Contacts	RCH	0v
8. Contacts	$CC1$	0v
9. Contacts	$CC2$	0v
10. Motor	MCF	230v
11. Motor	$MC1$	230v

Problem 1.

STEP 1. Has been completed.

STEPS 2 and 3. One compressor is running, voltage and fuses are alright.

STEP 4. Second stage compressor is not running.

STEP 5.

☐ Check compressor terminals R to C. If 230v is read, the compressor is defective or the internal protector is open.

☐ Check between the load side of contacts CC_2 and CC_2. If 230v is read, there is an open wire between the compressor and the contactor.

☐ Check the line side of contacts CC_2 and CC_2. If 230v is read, the contacts are open.

If no voltage is available, there is a line open to the contactor from L_1 or L_2.

☐ Check coil CC_2 in the 24v circuit. If 24v is read, the coil is defective.

If no voltage is available, there is a wire open from terminal C_2 to the coil.

Problem 2.

STEP 1. Has been completed.

STEPS 2 and 3. One compressor is running, voltage and fuses are alright.

STEP 4. First stage compressor is not running.

STEP 5.

☐ The schematic shows that the condenser fan motor is wired parallel to the first stage compressor. Therefore, the contacts are alright.

☐ Check between terminals R and C on compressor 1. If 230v is read, the compressor is defective.

If no voltage is available, a wire is open between the contacts and the compressor.

Problem 3.

STEP 1. Has been completed.

STEPS 2 and 3. Compressor is running, voltage and fuses are alright.

STEP 4. Blower motor is not running.

STEP 5.

☐ Check for voltage at blower motor terminals MCH. If 230v is read, the motor is defective.

☐ Check across relay contacts RCH. If 230v is read, the contacts are open.

If no voltage is available, a wire is open to L_1 or L_2.

☐ Check across coil RCH. If 24v is read, the coil is defective.

☐ Check across contacts RC. If 24v is read, the contacts are open.

If no voltage is available, a wire is open to terminal V.

☐ Check coil RC. If 24v is read, the coil is defective.

☐ Check across terminals V to F on the terminal block. If 24v is read, the thermostat is open.

If no voltage is read, a wire is open from V to coil RC.

HEATING

1. Coil RCB		24v
2. Coil RCH		24v
3. Coil GV		24v
4. Coil GC		0v
5. Switch SGP		0v
6. Switch SS		0v
7. Switch SF		0v
8. Contacts RCB		0v
9. Contacts RCH		0v
10. Motor MCB		230v
11. Motor MCH		230v

Problem 1.

STEP 1. Has been completed.

STEPS 2 and 3. Check line voltage fuses and 2.5 amp fuse at transformer secondary. Check for 24v at transformer secondary.

STEP 4. Burner will not ignite.

STEP 5.

☐ Check the gas valve. If 24v is read, the gas valve is defective.

☐ Check across the safety switches: LS, ALS, SS. If 24v is read across any switch, that switch is open.

If LS or ALS is open, give them time to reset.

☐ If SS is open, check the MCB motor terminals. If 230v is read, the motor is defective

☐ Check across contacts RCB. If 230v is read, the contacts are open

☐ Check coil RCB. If 24v is read, the coil is open.

☐ Check switch SGP. If 24v is read, the switch is open.

If no voltage is available, a wire is open from H to the switch.

Problem 2.

STEP 1. Has been completed.

STEPS 2 and 3. With partial operation, voltage and fuses are alright.

STEP 4. Blower will not operate while heating.

STEP 5.

☐ The schematic shows that the blower motor is controlled by a fan switch in the 24v circuit.

☐ Check the SF switch. If 24v is read, the switch is open.

If no voltage is available, there is a wire open from terminal V to the switch.

Problem 3.

STEP 1. Has been completed.

STEPS 2 and 3. Voltage and fuses are alright.

STEP 4. Pilot flame will not ignite.

STEP 5.

☐ Check the glow coil. If 2.5v is read, the coil is defective.

☐ Check across relay contacts RAP. If voltage is read, the contacts are open.

If no voltage is available, a wire is open from the transformer to the RAP relay or the 2.5v transformer secondary is open.

WILLIAMSON

1. Motor relay coil	◯ MOTOR RELAY	**24v**
2. Flame relay coil	FLAME RELAY	**24v**
3. Fan motor	FAN MTR.	**115v**
4. Burner motor	BRNR. MTR.	**115v**
5. Fan switch	FAN	**0v**
6. Motor relay contacts	MOTOR RELAY	**0v**
7. Flame relay contacts		**24v**
8. Filter flag		**24v**
9. Humidistat (open)	HUMIDISTAT	**24v**

Problem 1.

STEP 1. Has been completed.

STEPS 2 and 3. With partial operation, voltage and fuses are alright.

STEP 4. Fan motor will not run during cooling cycle.

STEP 5.

☐ Check the fan motor. If 115v is read at the the terminals, the motor is defective.

☐ Check the fan relay contacts. If 115v is read, the contacts are open.

If no voltage is present, there is a broken wire.

☐ Check the fan relay coil in the 24v circuit. If 24v is read, the coil is defective.

☐ Check the thermostat across terminals R to G. If 24v is read, the thermostat is defective.

If 24v is not read, there is a broken wire, usually from G to the fan relay coil.

GE

COOLING

1. Coil		**24v**
2. Coil		**24v**
3. Coil		**24v**
4. Switch		**0v**
5. Switch		**0v**
6. Switch		**0v**
7. I.D. Fan Motor A to M		**230v**
8. CPR Motor C to R		**230v**
9. O.D. Fan Motor HI to WHITE		**230v**

Problem 2.

STEP 1. Has been completed.

STEPS 2 and 3. Burner motor runs, voltage and fuses are alright.

STEP 4. Burner motor and ignition cease after 45 seconds.

STEP 5.

☐ If the flame detector does not see a flame in 45 seconds, the burner and ignition will cut-out in 45 seconds. First, check the oil supply.

☐ Check the limit switch. If 115v is read, the limit is open and may be defective.

☐ Check the flame detector following the manufacturer's recommendations.

Problem 1.

STEP 1. Has been completed.

STEPS 2 and 3. Compressor is running, voltage and fuses are alright.

STEP 4. Hot rather than cool air during summer operation.

STEP 5.

☐ The schematic shows that the switchover valve is energized with the first stage of cooling, the second stage starts the compressor.

Check for voltage across the switchover coil (SC). If 24v is read, the coil is defective or the switchover valve is stuck in the heating position.

☐ Check the low voltage terminal board from R to O. If voltage is read, the thermostat is open.

☐ If no voltage is read from between the thermostat and the switchover coil, there is a broken wire.

Problem 2.

STEP 1. Has been completed.

STEPS 2 and 3. Indoor fan is running, voltage and fuses are alright.

STEP 4. Compressor and outdoor fan are not running.

STEP 5.

☐ Check from C to R on the compressor motor and from Red and Black to White on the outdoor fan motor. If voltage is read the motors are defective or the internal protectors are open.

☐ Check for voltage across contacts MS-1A and MS-1B. If 230v is read, the contacts are open. If no voltage is read, look for a broken wire.

☐ Check coil MS in the 24v circuit. If 24v is read, the coil is defective.

☐ Check the high pressure cutout. If 24v is read, this safety device is open.

☐ On the low voltage terminal board, check from R to Y. If 24v is read, the thermostat is open.

If voltage is read from Y to the MS coil, look for broken wires between these two points.

Problem 3.

STEP 1. Has been completed.

STEPS 2 and 3. Compressor is running, voltage and fuses are alright.

STEP 4. Outdoor fan is not running. The indoor fan is running and the compressor is cycling on the high pressure cutout.

STEP 5.

☐ Check for voltage between Black and Red to White at the outdoor fan motor. If 230v is read the motor is defective.

☐ Check contacts MS-1B. If 230v is read, the contactor is defective.

If voltage is not present, look for a broken wire to the motor.

HEATING

1. Coil		24v
2. Coil		24v
3. Coil		0v
4. Contact DFC to HI		0v
5. Contacts		0v
6. Contacts		0v
7. Contacts		0v
8. Contacts		0v

Problem 1.

STEP 1. Has been completed.

STEPS 2 and 3. Outdoor fan is running, voltage and fuses are alright.

STEP 4. Compressor is not running. Fans are running.

STEP 5.

☐ Check for voltage at compressor terminals R and C. If 230v is read, the compressor is defective or the internal protector is open.

☐ Check contacts MS-1A. If 230v is read, the contacts are open and the contactor is defective.

☐ If no voltage is present, a wire is broken between the motor and the contacts.

Problem 2.

STEP 1. Has been completed.

STEPS 2 and 3. Check voltages, including the 24v secondary, and the fuses.

STEP 4. Nothing is running.

STEP 5.

☐ Check across the compressor terminals R to C, the outdoor fan motor terminals Black and Red to White, indoor fan terminals Black to Black. If 230v is read, the motor is defective.

If no voltage is present, there is a broken wire between the fuses and the motors.

☐ Check across contacts MS-1A, MS-1B, and F-1. If voltage is read, the contacts are open.

☐ Check the contactor coil MS and the fan coil F in the 24v circuit. If 24v is read, the coils are defective.

☐ Check the terminal board from terminal R to terminals Y and G. If 24v is read, the thermostat is open.

If no voltage is present, a wire is open from R to the transformer secondary.

Problem 3.

STEP 1. Has been completed.

STEPS 2 and 3. Each duct heater has a separate power supply. Check both voltage and fuses.

STEP 4. One duct heater will not operate. Contacts TSH-2 are closed. All motors are operating.

STEP 5.

☐ Check voltage at the duct heater terminals. If 230v is read, the heater is defective.

☐ Check for voltage across the outdoor thermostat ODT contacts. If 24v is read, the thermostat is open.

If no voltage is present, a wire is open between the ODT and the heater control relay.

Author Stanley Aglow has had more than 15 years experience as an installation and service supervisor and writes a regular electrical service column for the *Air Conditioning, Heating and Refrigeration News.*